Pool Lifeguard

TRAINING MANUAL

Brian V Sims   Edited by Andy Farquarson

THE ROYAL LIFE SAVING SOCIETY UK

Mosby Lifeline

St. Louis Baltimore Carlsbad Philadelphia
London Sydney Tokyo Toronto

Pool Lifeguard
TRAINING MANUAL

Brian V Sims

Edited by Andy Farquarson

THE ROYAL LIFE SAVING SOCIETY UK

Publisher: John A. Hirst

Vice President, Publishing Technology: Adam Phillips

Sales and Marketing Director: Christy J Wilson

Production Director: Susan Walby

Production Controller: Gudrun Hughes

Book Design: Studio Montage

Photography: Tim Fisher

Author: Brian V Sims

Edited by: Andy Farquarson

Editorial Advisory Board: Andrew Ebben (Safety Officer, Birmingham City Council), Jill Franks (ISRM Technical Information Forum and Watford Council), Tony Jones (RLSS UK and Metropolitan Borough of Wirral), Stephen Lear (Director, RLSS UK), Steven Taylor (Fitness Express Ltd).

First Edition 1989
Revised and reprinted 1993
Second edition 1997

Composition by Studio Montage, St. Louis, U.S.A.

Printing and binding by Grafos S. A. Arte sobre papel, Barcelona, Spain

ISBN 0-7234-3057-8

PREFACE

The Royal Life Saving Society UK has long been Britain's premier provider of training for swimming pool lifeguards. Following our major contribution to the Sports Council/HSE publication *Safety in Swimming Pools*, RLSS UK formulated and launched the National Pool Lifeguard Training Programme in 1988. The programme was a major step forward in the field and RLSS UK's National Pool Lifeguard Qualification is now the leisure industry's standard requirement.

Pool Lifeguarding, RLSS UK's authoritative lifeguard training manual, was first published in 1989. We produced the supplementary publication *Aquatic Spinal Cord Injury Management* in 1993, now in its second edition. A third RLSS UK book, *Life Support*, covers the techniques of cardiopulmonary resuscitation and basic life support.

Since *Pool Lifeguarding* was first published, swimming has become an increasingly popular recreation. Swimming pools have blossomed from the traditional rectangular tank into multi-use centres with a host of exciting new features. Legislation governing swimming pools, their managers and operators, and lifeguards has increased. These developments have emphasised the importance of pool lifeguarding and have also extended the lifeguard's role and responsibilities.

Hence the need for this new edition. Retitled *Pool Lifeguard*, extensively rewritten and expanded, it takes full account of the most up-to-date innovations in pools and their use. Although its primary purpose is to support candidates training for their National Pool Lifeguard Qualification, I believe it will also be an invaluable resource for anyone connected with or interested in aquatic leisure.

This edition of *Pool Lifeguard* contains much more information about resuscitation and management of spinal injuries than its predecessor. The RLSS UK book *Aquatic Spinal Cord Injury Management* is still in print, while a new expanded version of *Life Support* has just been published by Mosby Lifeline. Both titles are available from RLSS UK Enterprises Ltd.

Whether you are a prospective lifeguard, a trainer, a pool operator, a leisure manager, or otherwise involved with swimming pools, you will find this book interesting and informative. Above all, I hope it will contribute towards a safer, more enjoyable environment for all swimmers and pool users.

Ken White

Chairman, RLSS UK National Lifeguard and Rescue Committee

ACKNOWLEDGEMENTS

e wish to thank: John Hirst, Christy Wilson and Fiona Alderman at Mosby Lifeline; Studio Montage; RLSS UK staff at Mountbatten House; Dr A J Handley, RLSS UK President and Chief Medical Advisor; Ken White, Chairman of RLSS UK National Lifeguard and Rescue Committee, K Gee of Guild of Casualties; Ann Dodd at Barnsley Metropolitan Borough Council and lifeguards at Barnsley Metrodome; Maureen Harrison and lifeguards of Blyth Lifeguard Club; lifeguards and staff at The Leys Sports Centre, Redditch; Peter Whitall for first aid information; and Tim Fisher for photography.

We gratefully acknowledge reference material produced by the Health and Safety Executive, the Sports Council, the Institute of Sport and Recreation Management, the Amateur Swimming Association and the Institute of Swimming Teachers and Coaches.

The Royal Life Saving Society UK, Mountbatten House, Studley, Warwickshire B80 7NN.
Telephone: 01527 853943
Fax: 01527 854453

AUTHOR'S NOTE

The main purpose of *Pool Lifeguard* is to support candidates training for the Foundation Module of the National Pool Lifeguard Qualification (NPLQ). But it is also essential reading for trainers, assessors, lifeguards and anyone else involved in the operation or management of swimming pools. In particular, qualified lifeguards will find *Pool Lifeguard* invaluable to support their in-service training and keep their skills up to date.

We have endeavoured to make this book easy and enjoyable to read and use. It is written in a clear, concise style and the contents are arranged in a logical manner. At the beginning of each chapter you will find a preview of its contents and at the end a 'test yourself' section so you can check that you've grasped the key points.

Abbreviations throughout the book are written out in full at first use and also defined in the glossary for quick reference. The most common are NOP for Normal Operating Procedures, EAP for Emergency Action Plan and CPR for Cardiopulmonary Resuscitation.

Although this book is as comprehensive as possible, a single volume can't cover all the permutations of swimming pools and their facilities so the contents of *Pool Lifeguard* are inevitably generic. Each pool has its own unique features and the Professional (Site Specific) Module of NPLQ training reflects this. However, just because this book may not cover all the features of a particular pool, it does not mean they can be ignored by the lifeguards or operator at that site.

There are various laws regulating swimming pools, notably the Health and Safety at Work Act 1974 and the Management of Health and Safety at Work Regulations 1992. All lifeguards and trainers (and, of course, leisure managers and pool operators) have legal responsibilities and should read the summary of the law's demands in Chapter One. Where appropriate, specific legislation is also referred to in the text.

Safety in Swimming Pools was a prime source for the first edition of *Pool Lifeguarding* and it has proved equally invaluable to us while writing this second edition. We have also consulted much other useful reference material, including lifeguard training manuals from around the world.

Each year the leisure industry is growing, swimming pool facilities are developing and medical knowledge is advancing. So future editions of this book will require revision and updating. This is where you, the reader, can help. Please write to us at RLSS UK with your comments and suggestions on how we can make *Pool Lifeguard* even more useful to you. Your letters will be warmly welcomed.

Contents

COMMUNICATION BETWEEN LIFEGUARDS

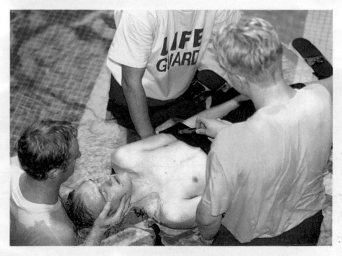

1

The Pool Lifeguard

THIS CHAPTER COVERS:

- KEY FUNCTIONS OF POOL LIFEGUARDS; THE DIFFERENCE BETWEEN LIFEGUARDS AND LIFESAVERS; TEAMWORK; LIFEGUARD UNIFORMS AND PERSONAL EQUIPMENT.

- TYPES OF SWIMMING POOL; RISK ASSESSMENT; NORMAL OPERATING PROCEDURES (NOP) AND THE EMERGENCY ACTION PLAN (EAP).

- ACCIDENT PREVENTION; HAZARDS; SIGNS; EDUCATING AND SUPERVISING POOL USERS.

- TRAINING AND ASSESSING POOL LIFEGUARDS; THE NATIONAL POOL LIFEGUARD QUALIFICATION (NPLQ); IN-SERVICE TRAINING.

- LIFEGUARDS AND THE LAW; THE DUTY OF CARE; THE HEALTH AND SAFETY AT WORK ACT AND OTHER LEGISLATION; ENFORCEMENT.

The Pool Lifeguard

SWIMMING POOLS vary enormously both in their size and layout and in the facilities and activities they provide. But whether visiting the smallest hotel pool or the largest multi–featured leisure centre, one thing pool users *do* expect is adequate lifeguard provision. They want swimming pools that are safely managed by smartly turned–out, well–trained, qualified lifeguards who will assist and protect them.

What sort of people choose to train as lifeguards? Well, some will have a background in swimming at various levels. Others will have taken higher education courses in sports and leisure subjects. The candidates will be good communicators who enjoy helping other people. They will need to be alert, have good powers of concentration and have a sense of humour (Fig 1-1).

The key functions of a pool lifeguard are:

- to keep a close watch over the pool and the users;
- to anticipate problems;
- to identify emergencies quickly and take appropriate action;
- to supervise diving or other pool activity when required;
- to carry out rescues and other emergency action when necessary;
- to give immediate first aid to any casualty; and
- to communicate with pool users and colleagues when performing these tasks.

LIFESAVERS AND LIFEGUARDS

Members of the public often assume the terms 'lifesaver' and 'lifeguard' amount to the same thing. But there are important differences.

Lifesavers are trained bystanders who respond to an emergency after it has occurred. They usually act alone or enlist the help of other bystanders, rather than act as part of a team.

FIGURE 1-1
LIFEGUARDS MUST ENJOY HELPING PEOPLE.

Lifeguards, by contrast, are team members trained in accident prevention, rescue and first aid. They will be on the lookout for potential dangers or accidents and will take action to prevent them developing.

Lifeguards are responsible for supervising swimming pools and ensuring the users' safety. This brings them into constant contact with the public and they have to deal with a wide range of ages, backgrounds and abilities (Fig. 1-2). So they are trained to be tolerant, supportive and courteous. And because they must ensure that pool users follow safety rules, lifeguards are also trained to be authoritative when the need arises.

Lifeguards always work to a pool's Written Operating Procedures. This means lifeguards will be specially trained to deal with incidents at the pool where they are working.

Some lifeguards are full–time employees, others work part time and some give their time voluntarily. Whether they are full time, part timers, temporary staff members or volunteers, their role and responsibility as lifeguards is the same.

The table below compares the responsibilities of lifeguards and lifesavers.

FIGURE 1-2
CONTACT WITH THE PUBLIC.

THE RESPONSIBILITIES OF LIFESAVERS AND LIFEGUARDS

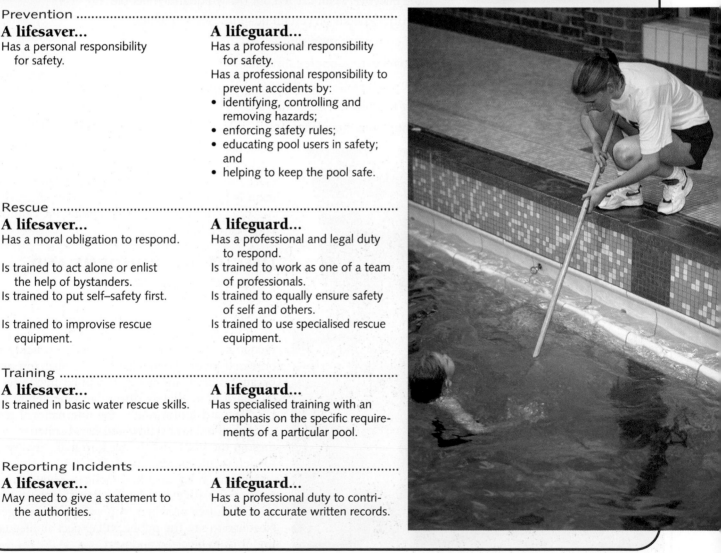

Prevention ....

A lifesaver...
Has a personal responsibility for safety.

A lifeguard...
Has a professional responsibility for safety.
Has a professional responsibility to prevent accidents by:
• identifying, controlling and removing hazards;
• enforcing safety rules;
• educating pool users in safety; and
• helping to keep the pool safe.

Rescue ....

A lifesaver...
Has a moral obligation to respond.

Is trained to act alone or enlist the help of bystanders.
Is trained to put self–safety first.

Is trained to improvise rescue equipment.

A lifeguard...
Has a professional and legal duty to respond.
Is trained to work as one of a team of professionals.
Is trained to equally ensure safety of self and others.
Is trained to use specialised rescue equipment.

Training ....

A lifesaver...
Is trained in basic water rescue skills.

A lifeguard...
Has specialised training with an emphasis on the specific requirements of a particular pool.

Reporting Incidents ....

A lifesaver...
May need to give a statement to the authorities.

A lifeguard...
Has a professional duty to contribute to accurate written records.

FIGURE 1-3
COMMUNICATION IS KEY IN EFFECTIVE LIFEGUARDING.

FIGURE 1-4
RESUSCITATION TEAM AT WORK.

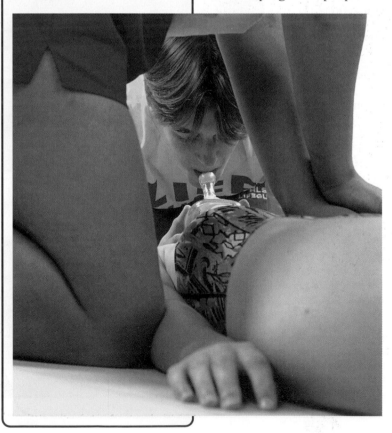

LIFEGUARDS AND TEAMWORK

Teamwork is an essential feature of lifeguarding. As we have seen, it is one of the things that distinguishes lifeguards from lifesavers. Obviously, the larger the pool, the larger the team but however small the venue, lifeguards should always work with the close support of their colleagues.

A well–trained team is more effective than its members would be if they were working as individuals. In an emergency, secure in the support of other team members, lifeguards can concentrate on their allotted task. This principle applies to all aspects of lifeguards' work and not just to dealing with emergencies (Fig. 1-3).

It is always possible that lifeguards may themselves get into difficulties or be injured during a rescue. Then the support of the team will be essential. That is why team working is an integral part of lifeguard training.

Sometimes, lifeguards may have to be on duty alone. RLSS UK does not believe this to be best practice. However, a Risk Assessment may establish that it is reasonable in certain specific circumstances.

In emergencies, team members can offer support in many ways. These include:

- summoning additional assistance from the emergency services (an ambulance, for instance);
- clearing the public from the pool when recovering a casualty; and
- assisting with cardiopulmonary resuscitation of a casualty (resuscitation is more effective when carried out by two qualified people, Fig. 1-4).

Teamwork depends on certain qualities. These include:

- good communication skills;
- willingness to support colleagues;
- readiness to work for others;
- being flexible and adaptable; and
- keeping other people informed.

Good team members always remember that their performance affects others and accept that they can't do everything by themselves. A successful team is built on a relationship of mutual trust and respect. The importance of teamwork cannot be emphasised too strongly.

LIFEGUARDS' UNIFORMS AND PERSONAL EQUIPMENT

Lifeguards should always wear a uniform when they are on duty. The uniform should be both distinctive and very 'visible' so pool users will easily recognise lifeguards and spot them quickly in a crowded pool. High visibility is also important because other team members will be able to see the lifeguard immediately during an emergency. RLSS UK lifeguard uniform uses the international rescue colours of red and yellow and has distinctive markings on the front and the back to make it very easy to identify lifeguards (Fig. 1-5).

Uniforms must also be practical. They must not restrict the lifeguards' movement, either during normal duties or when responding to emergency. Needless to say, the public will expect all lifeguards' uniforms to be clean and neat.

FIGURE 1-5
UNIFORMS NEED TO BE DISTINCTIVE AND HIGHLY VISIBLE.

Lifeguards should not wear wrist watches or jewellery (such as ear rings, bracelets or chains) while they are on duty. Watches or jewellery could injure a casualty (or, for that matter, the lifeguard) when dealing with an emergency or performing a rescue.

Lifeguards on duty usually carry a few items of personal equipment. The most common is a whistle to attract pool users' attention and give signals. Most lifeguards will carry, or keep close at hand, a throwbag and a torpedo buoy. Sometimes lifeguards also carry items such as sterile dressings in a waterproof pack and a resuscitation mask. Whatever personal equipment lifeguards carry, it must not hinder them or restrict their movements (Fig. 1-6).

FIGURE 1-6
EQUIPMENT SHOULD NOT RESTRICT YOUR MOVEMENTS.

FIGURE 1-7
A LARGE FREE-FORM LEISURE COMPLEX POOL; **B** SMALL HOTEL POOL; **C** OPEN AIR LIDO;
D RECTANGULAR POOL.

SWIMMING POOLS AND WRITTEN PROCEDURES

Because the size, layout and facilities of pools vary so much, training for the RLSS UK National Pool Lifeguard Qualification (NPLQ) is divided into two modules. The Foundation Module covers the training applicable to any type of pool and it familiarises lifeguards with the variety of pool types they may encounter. They learn about the range and diversity of pools without addressing any particular site.

The Professional (Site Specific) Module, by contrast, ensures that the lifeguards at a particular pool are aware of its individual characteristics, unique features and any particular hazards. Most importantly, they are trained to implement the pool's specific Written Operating Procedures.

The illustrations on this page show just what a wide variety of pool types lifeguards may encounter. Pools range from the familiar basic rectangular type to the very sophisticated free–form leisure complex pools that often feature a range of activities such as flumes and wave machines (Fig. 1-7 A–D).

WRITTEN OPERATING PROCEDURES

No matter how large or small a pool is, the operator must provide Written Operating Procedures and ensure the lifeguards are trained and competent to implement them.

Written Operation Procedures usually consist of a Normal Operating Procedure (NOP) and an Emergency Action Plan (EAP). The first stage in compiling these is to carry out a Risk Assessment of the pool and its environs. The Management of Health and Safety Regulations 1992 requires pool operators to carry out such an assessment.

A Risk Assessment is essential to drawing up an accident prevention strategy. It includes:

- identifying hazards;
- envisaging the sort of emergencies that could arise;
- evaluating the consequences of various incidents;
- assessing the likelihood of such incidents arising; and
- deciding what practical steps can be taken to lessen the risks.

Because it is essential that lifeguards understand the principles behind the procedures, the Foundation Module of the NPLQ includes training in understanding Written Operating Procedures.

As well as this general understanding of procedures, lifeguards working or training at a particular pool must be fully conversant with its specific NOP and EAP. Inadequate knowledge of Written Operating Procedures has often been identified by investigations and inquests to have been a contributory factor in accidents at swimming pools. This is why so much emphasis is given to the subject during lifeguard training.

NORMAL OPERATING PROCEDURES

All the lifeguards working at a pool must be thoroughly familiar with its Normal Operating Procedure. The NOP sets out how the pool should be operated on a day to day basis. It plays a vital part in ensuring the safety of pool users and staff members (Fig. 1-8). The NOP takes into account:

- the physical characteristics of the pool and its layout (Fig 1-9);
- particular hazards;
- the way in which equipment is operated;
- the pool's policies, rules and regulations; and
- the role of the lifeguard team in the safe management of the pool.

The law requires that NOPs are regularly reviewed by pool operators and updated if necessary. Best practice includes the lifeguard team in the review process. The NOP should also be reviewed after an accident, taking into account the findings of any investigation or report, so that similar incidents may be avoided in future.

Lifeguards arriving at a pool to work or train will have been introduced to the principles of NOPs in their Foundation Module. They will receive more specific instruction about the pool's NOP and how to implement it during their Professional (Site Specific) Module training.

FIGURE 1-8
A CHAT ABOUT SAFETY.

FIGURE 1-9
POOL LAYOUT AND REGULATIONS.

NORMAL OPERATING PROCEDURES

Normal Operating Procedures are usually composed around this framework:

• The details of the pool, including its dimensions and a plan of the building.

• An assessment of all potential risks.

• How the pool users are handled, including safety instruction and education, controlling access and enforcing safety rules.

• The maximum number of users permitted in the pool (Fig. 1-10).

• First aid supplies and training.

• The conditions for hire to outside organisations.

• Details of alarm systems and emergency equipment, and maintenance arrangements for them.

• The lifeguards' duties, including the special supervision requirements for equipment.

• The systems of work, including:
—lines of supervision;
—call out procedures;
—work rotation (if applicable); and
—the maximum duration of pool side duty periods.

• The provision of lifeguard training.

• The numbers of lifeguards required for particular activities.

FIGURE 1-10
THE NUMBER OF SWIMMERS SHOULD NOT EXCEED THE MAXIMUM PERMITTED.

The panel above outlines the principles upon which NOPs are usually based. An individual pool's NOP would obviously include much more detailed and specific information.

EMERGENCY ACTION PLANS

All the lifeguards working at a pool must be thoroughly familiar with its Emergency Action Plan. The detailed provisions of an EAP are tailored to the pool it applies to. It sets out **what** needs to be done in a given emergency situation, **who** should do it and **how** it should be done. The EAP takes into account:

• the individual characteristics and features of the pool and its building;

• any specific hazards of the site;

• the number of staff available and their level of training;

• the extent and location of first aid facilities; and

• the type and location of other emergency equipment.

Lifeguards arriving at a pool to work or train will have been introduced to the principles of EAPs in their Foundation Module. They will receive more specific instruction about the pool's EAP and how to implement it during their Professional (Site Specific) Module training.

Emergency Action Plans are drawn up according to certain general principles and these appear in the panel on the next page. Each pool's individual EAP will obviously include much more detailed and specific information.

EMERGENCY ACTION PLAN

Emergency Action Plans are usually composed around this framework:

- Links with the NOP to make clear the number, location and function of all staff on duty.

- The number of lifeguards needed to deal with an incident and what response is expected from the public.

- Details of who:
  —is in charge immediately an incident occurs;
  —is responsible for summoning the emergency services; and
  —is in charge after further assistance has been sought.

- Details of the system of communication during an incident (Fig. 1-11).

- The type and location of emergency equipment.

- The key tasks in dealing with an emergency.

- The key steps in dealing with an emergency (Fig. 1-12).

- The scope of first aid provision.

- The procedures for handling casualties and for their aftercare.

- How to handle public announcements and give information to the police, press, families and other legitimate enquirers.

- The procedures for compiling reports of incidents.

- The procedure for replenishing or replacing used supplies or equipment.

- Consideration of additional local factors to ensure the plan is comprehensive.

FIGURE 1-11
ONE PERSON SUMMONS
EMERGENCY SERVICES.

FIGURE 1-12
TAKING ACTION.

ACCIDENT PREVENTION

Preventing accidents is a pool lifeguard's first priority. Effective accident prevention makes a swimming pool a safer and more enjoyable place for both pool users and staff. The NOP plays a key part in accident prevention by identifying risks and setting out how activities should be conducted to ensure safety (Fig. 1-15 on facing page).

Prevention is always better than cure, especially when the cure is a rescue or first aid treatment. This sort of cure usually means that prevention measures have been inadequate or have failed. Cure is a very poor second to prevention because it diverts lifeguards from their routine supervision and observation. A serious incident may lead to permanent injury or incapacity. Even a successful rescue can have a lasting psychological effect on the casualty, the rescuer, or both of them.

There are three main aspects to accident prevention. They are:

- a thorough Risk Assessment and Written Operating Procedures that are clearly understood by all staff;
- educating pool users in water safety and the rules governing use of the pool; and
- supervising pool users and maintaining order.

We have already looked at Risk Assessments and Written Operating Procedures. These affect education and supervision, safety rules and how they are communicated to the public.

PREVENTION THROUGH EDUCATION—HAZARDS

No swimming pool is entirely without hazards. Good pool design, proper maintenance of the pool and its equipment, the provisions of the NOP and, above all, effective lifeguard supervision all help to reduce the risks. However, some hazards will always remain and these may not always be obvious to the public.

Some hazards result from the way people use the pool. These include:

- pushing or crowding at entrances;
- running on the pool side;
- 'bomb diving' (Fig. 1-13);
- boisterous behaviour; and
- lack of consideration for other users.

Other hazards are physical. They include:

- deep water;
- slippery surfaces;
- flumes, chutes and slides (Fig. 1-14);
- underwater drain and outlet covers
- wave–making machine outlets;
- diving boards;
- floating equipment; and
- noise from water jets and turbulence.

Educating the public about these hazards is a major part of accident prevention. It can be done through written material or through supervision by lifeguards and other staff members. More detailed information on hazards can be found in Chapter Two.

FIGURE 1-13
BE AWARE OF THE DIVERS AND JUMPERS FROM THE BOARD.

FIGURE 1-14
WATER SLIDES CAN PRESENT SPECIAL HAZARDS.

FIGURE 1-15 PREVENTING ACCIDENTS HAS FIRST PRIORITY.

FIGURE 1-16
SYMBOLS CAN CONVEY
THE MESSAGE MORE
CLEARLY THAN WORDS.

FIGURE 1-17
CHILDREN OFTEN CLIMB
ON POOL FEATURES.

PREVENTION THROUGH EDUCATION—SIGNS

Written pool user education can take various forms. Signs are one of the most common ways of conveying safety information to pool users. Other methods might include handing pool users leaflets as they arrive or displaying prominent posters.

There are many uses for signs. The most common include marking the depth of water, prohibiting certain activities, calling attention to specific hazards and giving instructions on how to use equipment safely.

Signs need not always be written—sometimes symbols and pictograms can convey the message more clearly than words (Fig. 1-16).

All signs must:

• be legible and clearly printed;

• use simple, unambiguous language and clear symbols;

• be appropriately positioned in relation to the hazard they refer to; and

• be sited so that they are easily seen by all pool users.

Signs should comply with the Safety Signs and Signals Regulations 1996 and noted in RoSPA's National Water Safety Committee leaflet. Lifeguards should always ensure that signs are not obscured by equipment, clothing and so on and are kept clean.

PREVENTION THROUGH SUPERVISION

Lifeguards are in the front line of pool user education. That is one of the reasons they must be good communicators. They can educate pool users about the hazards and risks associated with a particular pool or activity, and about water safety generally.

In many cases, pool users may be unaware of the safety rules and ignore them unintentionally (Fig. 1-17). On other occasions they may deliberately flout the rules, and firmer, more direct, intervention by lifeguards may be needed. In either case, tact and diplomacy are called for. A smile and a friendly word is usually far more effective than a bossy or authoritarian approach.

When lifeguards are dealing with individual pool users, their attention may be distracted from the pool side. They should make sure that another member of the team takes over responsibility for that area of supervision. The NOP will outline the procedure lifeguards should follow when they have to enforce the safety rules and it will also set out how support may be summoned if it is needed.

When supervising the pool, lifeguards should avoid being so restrictive that pool users don't enjoy their visit. And if such features as flumes, chutes and slides are to be exciting (especially for younger pool users) there has to

be an *illusion* of risk (Fig. 1-18). Lifeguards must ensure that there is no *real* risk — but preferably without breaking the illusion.

Accident prevention by supervision relies on lifeguards being vigilant, attentive and alert at all times. They should be pro–active rather than reactive — that is, they must not sit back and let a potentially dangerous situation develop but must take early action to prevent it. See Normal Operating Procedures box on page 8.

Effective supervision requires specific skills. These include:

* recognition of people in difficulty;
* positioning;
* scanning; and
* communication.

These skills are explained in more detail in Chapter Two.

TRAINING

Lifeguards must receive comprehensive, high quality training from qualified trainers (Fig. 1-19). RLSS UK is Britain's principle provider of training for swimming pool lifeguards and the National Pool Lifeguard Training Programme is now universally recognised as the industry standard. This programme is continually developed and refined so that it meets the needs of the leisure industry, the demands of pool users and the requirements of the law.

Lifeguard training is divided into two parts. The generic Foundation Module is prepared and delivered by RLSS UK qualified Trainer/Assessors. The Professional (Site Specific) Module is prepared and delivered by Institute of Sport and Recreation Management (ISRM) qualified Trainers. Candidates who successfully complete both Modules gain the National Pool Lifeguard Qualification (NPLQ).

There are certain requirements before prospective lifeguards start training. Candidates should be:

* fit and healthy;
* completely confident in deep water;
* able to swim 50 metres in one minute or under;
* able to swim 100 metres on their front without pausing;
* able to swim 100 metres on their back without pausing; and
* able to dive from the surface of the water to a depth of not less than 1.5 metres.

Some prior knowledge of lifesaving and basic life support is also desirable. Training for RLSS UK's Bronze Medallion is a useful preparation for candidates.

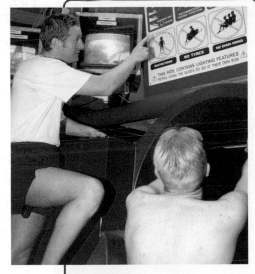

FIGURE 1-18
CONTROLLING FLUME.

FIGURE 1-19
LIFEGUARD TRAINING SESSION.

FIGURE 1-20
LIFEGUARDS WORKING AS A TEAM.

TRAINING SYLLABUS

The list below gives an idea of the scope of training for the Foundation Module of the NPLQ. It is by no means exhaustive and full details are contained in the current NPLQ syllabus which is available from RLSS UK.

NPLQ Foundation Module training includes:

- how to work effectively as part of a lifeguard team (Fig. 1-20);
- how to maintain observation of a pool and users;
- how to supervise pool users;
- how to communicate effectively with pool users and other team members;
- how to effect a prompt rescue;
- how to use emergency equipment;
- how to enter the water safely and dive to the deepest part of the pool;
- how to recover and land a pool user who is in difficulty (Fig. 1-21);
- how to perform resuscitation by expired air ventilation and by cardiopulmonary resuscitation;
- how to use resuscitation equipment where it is provided; and
- how to provide emergency first aid.

The panel below is a guide to the minimum duration of Foundation Module training. These times are the minimum and many courses provide additional hours. Training for the Professional (Site Specific) Module and in–service training are additional to this minimum.

ASSESSMENT

After Foundation Module training is complete, candidates are assessed by an independent RLSS UK Trainer/Assessor. Successful candidates are awarded their NPLQ Foundation Module.

Candidates will be tested on their:

- knowledge of water safety and pool emergency practices;
- understanding of the principles of NOPs and EAPs;
- knowledge of pool rescueequipment;
- practical rescue skills;
- practical cardio pulmonary resuscitation skills, using a manikin; and
- practical and theoretical first aid skills and knowledge.

MINIMUM DURATION OF FOUNDATION MODULE TRAINING

	Minimum times	
	New Courses	Renewal Courses
Theory		
Pool environment and safety	5 hours	2 hours
Practical (dry)		
Cardio pulmonary resuscitation and first aid	11 hours	8 hours
Practical (wet)		
Personal skills: immediate response	6 hours	4 hours
Team skills	5 hours	3 hours
Spinal cord injury management	6 hours	3 hours
Minimum Total		
	33 hours	20 hours

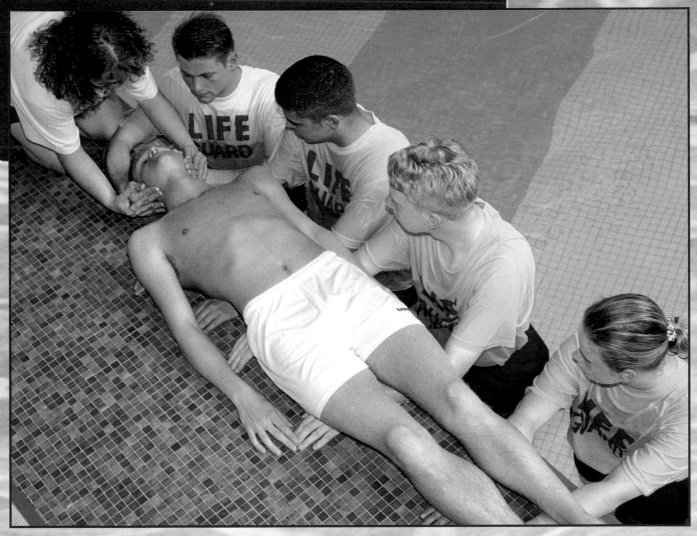

FIGURE 1-21 LIFEGUARDS PERFORM A LIFT-OUT RESCUE.

FIGURE 1-22
TRAINING IS IMPORTANT.

FIGURE 1-23
THE RLSS UK
LOG BOOK.

IN–SERVICE TRAINING

The law requires employers to provide training to ensure their staff remain competent to do their jobs. This means that pool lifeguards must receive regular in–service training to keep their knowledge and techniques up to date and abreast of developments (Fig. 1-22).

Even allowing for complex shift patterns in large leisure centres, one training session of at least an hour every three weeks should be the absolute minimum. Pool side rescue equipment should be included in the relevant training session, particularly for incident training.

Even if staffing levels are limited (for instance, in hotel pools), the operator should define the level of training needed to ensure effective lifeguard provision.

As well as in–service training, lifeguards must also maintain their general fitness and health. Pool operators should also arrange lifeguard team meetings to ensure full and continued understanding of the NOP and EAP.

A full training record must be kept and the NPLQ Log Book is ideal for the purpose. Records should include the lifeguard's name, details of the venue, the date and duration of the session, and details of the lifeguard's knowledge, skills and understanding of operational procedures. These records form an important part of the Professional (Site Specific) evaluation for the NPLQ (Fig. 1-23).

In–service training routines will obviously vary depending on the size of the pool and the range of activities. Skills that may form part of in–service training include:

- incident training;
- a dive to the deepest part of the pool to recover a submerged manikin;
- a timed rescue as described in the NPLQ syllabus;
- cardiopulmonary resuscitation training on manikins using a resuscitation kit if one is on site; and
- spinal cord injury management training using an RLSS UK–approved spineboard if one is on site.

LIFEGUARDS AND THE LAW

Lifeguards need a basic understanding of laws and regulations which affect them when carrying out their duties. Laws made by parliament are called primary legislation and are usually referred to as 'Acts'. Detailed provisions may be added by ministers through a process called secondary legislation and these provisions, which have the force of law, are usually referred to as 'Regulations'. Although many codes of practice derive from Acts or Regulations, they also have the force of law.

DUTY OF CARE

As well as the specific requirements of Acts and Regulations, operators, managers and supervisors of swimming pools have a duty of care to anyone using the pool. They must take reasonable care to avoid actions or omissions which could reasonably be foreseen as likely to cause injury to any pool user or staff member.

If they fail to exercise their duty by not taking reasonable care to avoid foreseeable injuries, pool operators, managers, supervisors and lifeguards could be found to be negligent. Negligence is a likely basis of court action against a pool operators or their staff following an incident at a pool. However, criminal proceedings (or those following an industrial tribunal) are not uncommon.

THE HEALTH AND SAFETY AT WORK ACT 1974

This Act places obligations on pool operators and the lifeguards they employ. It requires employers to protect the health, safety and welfare of their employees while they are at work.

Among other things, this requirement includes:

*   providing and maintaining systems of work which are safe and without risk to health;
*   providing and maintaining premises, plant and equipment so that they are safe and without risk to health; and
*   providing information, instruction, training and supervision.

The obligation covers third parties (customers) as well as employees and requires employers to conduct their undertakings so that people not in their employment who may be affected are not exposed to risks to their health or safety.

The Act also puts obligations upon employees While at work, employees must take reasonable care of the health and safety of themselves and other persons who may be affected by their actions or omissions.

THE MANAGEMENT OF HEALTH AND SAFETY AT WORK REGULATIONS 1992

These regulations require employers to perform an assessment of the risks to which their employees or persons connected with their work are exposed and to reduce those risks and make any appropriate arrangements. If there are five or more employees, employers must record the findings of the Risk Assessment and the measures taken.

Employers must review the Risk Assessment if circumstances change or if it becomes out of date. They must also establish appropriate procedures to be followed in the event of serious or imminent danger.

Employers must provide training and instruction on the nature of hazards which might otherwise prove a danger to employees, including equipment. They must also provide employees with comprehensive information on any special occupational qualification or skills needed to carry out their work safely.

This means that every swimming pool must have a proper Risk Assessment and have Written Operating Procedures which take account of any risks and hazards

PROVISION AND USE OF WORK EQUIPMENT REGULATIONS 1992

Under these regulations, employers must ensure that:

*   equipment is suitable and properly maintained;
*   adequate training is provided; and
*   equipment conforms with EEC directives where applicable.

WORKPLACE (HEALTH, SAFETY AND WELFARE) REGULATIONS 1992

These regulations apply to places of work. They require employers to:

*   maintain the workplace and equipment in good repair;
*   ensure all outdoor work stations provide, so far as reasonably practical, protection from adverse weather;
*   enable the employee to leave the workplace swiftly in the event of an emergency;
*   ensure that employees are not likely to slip or fall;
*   provide protection where any person falling is likely to be injured; and
*   provide accessible and clean toilets and showers which are adequately ventilated, lit and equipped.

THE CONTROL OF SUBSTANCES HAZARDOUS TO HEALTH REGULATIONS 1994 (COSHH) AND AMENDMENT REGULATIONS 1996

These regulations require employers to:

*   undertake a Risk Assessment;
*   adequately control risk of exposure of employees to substances hazardous to health;
*   provide suitable protective equipment to control such exposure; and
*   provide information, instruction and training for any employee who may be exposed to such substances at work.

PERSONAL PROTECTIVE EQUIPMENT AT WORK REGULATIONS 1992

These regulations require employers to assess the job and ensure that suitable personal protective equipment is provided to employees who may be exposed to a health or safety risk at work. The regulations refer to all equipment and clothing which is intended to be worn or held by a person at work for safety reasons.

Choice of equipment should arise from a Risk Assessment, must be appropriate for the person and the task, be correctly fitting and properly maintained. Training should also be provided in its use.

The regulations also stipulate that employees provided with personal protective equipment must immediately report any loss or obvious defect.

SAFETY SIGNS AND SIGNALS REGULATIONS 1996

These regulations specify the function, shape, colouring and composition of signs.

Signs must conform to British Standard 5378 and be evident in all places of work, especially in those areas of swimming pools used by the public and supervised by lifeguards.

THE MANUAL HANDLING OPERATIONS REGULATIONS 1992

The regulations protect employees handling heavy loads at work, including handling casualties at swimming pools. They cover lifting, carrying, moving and supporting loads where that involves any risk to health and safety, particularly the risk of back injury to workers.

Employers are required to avoid the need for workers to handle loads manually where possible but where this cannot be avoided, they must take appropriate steps to reduce any risk to health or safety.

THE HEALTH AND SAFETY (FIRST AID) REGULATIONS 1981

These regulations require employers to:
- make adequate first aid provision for employees;
- provide first aid training for a suitable number of employees as determined by the HSE; and
- inform employees of the arrangements made, including the location of first aid equipment, facilities and personnel.

REPORTING OF INJURIES, DISEASES AND DANGEROUS OCCURRENCE REGULATIONS 1995 (RIDDOR)

These regulations require that any serious work–related or public accident is reported within seven days. The report is usually made to the HSE or to the nearest office of the Department of the Environment as appropriate.

Serious work–related accidents include those that result in:
- death;
- serious injury;
- loss of consciousness from lack of oxygen;

- poisoning requiring medical treatment; and
- a stay in hospital for longer than 24 hours.

A report must also be made when an accident results in anyone being off work for more than three consecutive working days. The regulations also require that records of a reported incident must be kept.

THE ELECTRICITY AT WORK REGULATIONS 1989

These detail safety measures when using electrical equipment and emphasise the importance of the correct electrical supply. Lifeguards should be familiar with the relevant provisions of these regulations.

THE FIRE PROTECTION ACT 1971

Lifeguards should be familiar with the provisions of the Fire Protection Act. They should note that all premises, including swimming pools, must be kept clean and tidy to reduce the risk of fire, and that exits should be kept clear and unlocked at all times (unless other specific provisions are set out in the Normal Operating Procedures).

Lifeguards must be familiar with fire alarm systems and the action set out in the Emergency Action Plans in the event of a fire. They must be trained to use various types of fire extinguisher and identify them by colour code to ensure the correct type is used.

At the time of writing, Workplace (Fire Precautions) Regulations are being prepared and these will probably include European Community rules regarding fire extinguishers.

ENFORCEMENT

The HSE has a duty to enforce laws governing health and safety at work. In general, as far as the leisure industry is concerned, the HSE monitors the public sector directly. It devolves responsibility for the private sector to the local authority, usually through environmental health departments.

Local authority and HSE inspectors have wide powers. They can enter premises at any reasonable time and can require anyone to answer any reasonable question about what is going on. They can also require pool operators to produce relevant documentation for inspection and copying.

Inspectors can take a wide range of actions if they discover something is wrong. Informal discussions often prove the best way to remedy a situation but the inspectors have two courses of action available in the case of a clear breach of the law.

They can issue an improvement notice which must state the contravention and give a time limit within which that required remedy must take place.

If inspectors believe that the breach of the law is so hazardous that the activity should not continue, they can issue a prohibition notice. A prohibition notice must state what is wrong and what action must be taken before the activity can be resumed.

In either case, the recipient can lodge an appeal in writing against the notice. The appeal is heard by a tribunal. The tribunal's decision can only be challenged if there has been an error of law.

A BRIEF SUMMARY

Written Operating Procedures are required by law and must:
- be based on a proper Risk Assessment:
- must be available to all staff;
- must be understood and followed by staff.

Training must be regular and must cover:
- equipment;
- cardiopulmonary resuscitation;
- all areas of the Normal Operating Procedure; and
- all areas of the Emergency Action Plan.

Records and logs must be kept of:
- all training sessions
- the duration and dates of training;
- first aid requirements;
- all incidents; and
- any re-qualifications.

Equipment must be:
- properly maintained;
- suitable for its purpose; and
- inspected and details recorded.

Qualifications must be:
- valid and up to date;
- kept at the appropriate level; and
- must be recognised.

Insurance must be adequate and provide appropriate cover at all times.

TEST YOURSELF

1. What is a lifeguard's first priority?
2. What are some other functions of a pool lifeguard?
3. List the key differences between a lifesaver and a lifeguard.
4. Why is teamwork so important to lifeguards?
5. Why should lifeguards wear a uniform?
6. What items of equipment do lifeguards carry or keep close at hand?
7. Why are Written Operating Procedures so important?
8. What two elements make up Written Operating Procedures?
9. Describe some of the things included in a Risk Assessment.
10. What do the initials NOP and EAP stand for?
11. Describe some hazards resulting from the way people use pools.
12. Describe some physical hazards found at pools.
13. What skills are required during supervision?
14. What does NPLQ stand for?
15. What is the minimum duration of basic lifeguard training?
16. Name the two Modules of the NPLQ training programme.
17. Why is in–service training needed?
18. What is a 'duty of care'?
19. What might establish negligence in a court?
20. Describe some provisions of the Health and Safety at Work Act 1974.
21. What do the initials COSHH and RIDDOR stand for?
22. Which law protects people lifting heavy loads?
23. What organisation is most likely to enforce laws relating to the workplace?

2

Lifeguard Operations

- CUSTOMER CARE AND SERVICE.

- PEOPLE HAZARDS; ACTIVITY HAZARDS; EQUIPMENT HAZARDS; LIFEGUARD HAZARDS; PHYSICAL HAZARDS

- SUPERVISION; OBSERVING THE POOL; INTENSIVE, EXTENSIVE AND COMBINED ZONING; SCANNING TECHNIQUES AND STRATEGIES.

- LIFEGUARD POSITIONS, HIGHCHAIRS AND FIXED POSITIONS; PATROLLING; ROTATION OF DUTIES.

- COMMUNICATING WITH POOL USERS; DISCIPLINE; COMPLAINTS.

- COMMUNICATION BETWEEN LIFEGUARDS BY SPEECH, WHISTLES AND HAND SIGNALS; USING RADIO TRANSCEIVERS AND TELEPHONES; VIDEO AND CCTV; AUDIBLE ALARMS.

Lifeguard Operations

SWIMMING POOL is the safest place to bathe for non-swimmers, novices and expert swimmers alike. To a large extent, this safety is ensured by the skill and knowledge of lifeguards.

To be effective, lifeguards must:

- be properly trained;
- keep their skills and knowledge up-to-date;
- be alert and vigilant when on duty;
- be trained in the Written Operating Procedures of the pool where they are working; and
- be aware of the laws and regulations governing pools and their operation.

In this chapter we look at how lifeguards deal with the public, supervise the pool, prevent accidents and ensure safety. As you read the following pages, remember that lifeguard operations must always follow the provisions of the Written Operating Procedures and are virtually always undertaken as part of a team.

CUSTOMER CARE

Lifeguards interact directly with pool users, their 'customers'. Although the principal aim of lifeguards is the protection of the public, they must also provide an all-round service to pool users.

Lifeguards can raise their pool's standards of service by:

- being passionate about high quality;
- making customers feel good about being at the pool;
- listening to and understanding customers;
- helping customers make the best decisions about how they use the pool; and
- always making that little extra effort.

Lifeguards are ambassadors. They play a key part in projecting the image of their swimming pool to the customers. They share this responsibility with other staff so, like all aspects of lifeguarding, customer care calls for teamwork.

As we have already seen, teamwork involves being flexible and adaptable, supporting colleagues, working with others to achieve a common goal, and communicating clearly with other team members. Remember that you cannot do everything yourself and that your performance will directly affect the whole team effort

Lifeguards should always be prepared to advise or direct pool users, even if the requests do not relate directly to swimming or water-based activities (Fig. 2-1). So lifeguards need a broad knowledge of their pool, its organisation and its facilities. Among other things, lifeguards should be able to help with:

- first aid;
- the location of facilities such as car parking and catering;
- the location of telephones, cloakrooms, toilets and so on;
- the facilities offered by the reception area;
- the arrangements for dealing with lost property;
- changing room facilities; and
- other services offered on site, such as a fitness centre.

FIGURE 2-1
LIFEGUARD DEALING
WITH THE PUBLIC.

HAZARDS

We can define a hazard as any physical object or installation or any activity involving people which might result in accident or injury. Hazards in and around the pool and those created, often unintentionally, by pool users have a profound effect on overall safety. Identifying hazards is the main purpose of risk assessment. Once identified, hazards must be balanced against the risk and the appropriate steps taken to minimise that risk.

Hazards can be divided into four categories, three created by people and one by the structure of the pool and its equipment. The four categories are:

• user hazards created by swimmers and others using the pool;

• activity hazards created by the way activities are undertaken;

• lifeguard hazards created by lifeguards or other staff; and

• physical hazards resulting from the design and structure of the pool and its equipment.

The hazards are, to some extent, dictated by the type of pool. For instance, a small rectangular pool where a few users are enjoying recreational swimming will present fewer hazards than a crowded large leisure centre with flumes, wave machines and so on.

Lifeguards must be trained to recognise both physical and people hazards in a wide range of pools. The Foundation Module of the NPLQ will give them an overview of the hazards commonly found at most pools. The Professional (Site Specific) Module will train them in the particular hazards to be found at the pool where they are working.

FIGURE 2-2 LIFEGUARDS ON DUTY.

PEOPLE HAZARDS

Lifeguards must be on the alert for danger at all times because early action may prevent a serious accident. If lifeguards observe and supervise pool users effectively, they can identify potential people hazards before an incident develops. That's why it is vital that lifeguards remain alert while they are on duty and observe pool users both before and after they enter the water.

By observing users before they enter the water, lifeguards can identify groups who may potentially be at risk (Fig. 2-3). They include:

- people under the influence of alcohol or drugs;
- people in poor health;
- the elderly and the very young;
- people who appear nervous or timid; and
- people with disabilities.

If pool users appear to be ill or intoxicated, lifeguards should prevent them from entering the water. Lifeguards stationed where pool users emerge from the changing rooms can quickly identify any of the groups above. In the case of premises with pool side changing, a position near the entrance would be more appropriate.

Once pool users are in the water, it may be more difficult to spot potential problems. Lifeguards should, however, look out for higher risk groups and keep a careful watch on them. They include:

- obviously weak swimmers;
- show-offs or particularly boisterous pool users;
- people supporting themselves on gutters or lane ropes;
- people wearing armbands or other buoyancy aids;
- children not accompanied by an adult; and
- adults 'teaching' youngsters, particularly diving into shallow water.

There are, of course, many other instances of people hazards (as distinct from hazards resulting from the activities people engage in). For instance, dangerous incidents can develop if weak swimmers inadvertently find themselves out of their depth and begin to panic. Lifeguards should always make sure that pool users are aware of depth signs but this type of incident can be difficult to prevent because pool users often consider warnings from lifeguards to be over-cautious.

Unattended small children are particularly at risk and should be watched very carefully (Fig. 2-4). Many pool and leisure centre operators don't allow children into the venue without an adult but some do. In either case, parents often leave small children playing unsupervised, believing the child to be reasonably competent and confident. Parents also sometimes leave older children to supervise younger siblings but the older ones may forget the responsibility as they enjoy their own activities. Although pool operators have overall responsibility for safety, parents must also consider safety of small children and lifeguards must always be alert to the hazard posed by unaccompanied youngsters. Both ISRM and RoSPA have issued guidelines on the safety of children in swimming pools.

Some pool users often stray into the area below diving boards or exits from flumes and slides and many accidents have resulted. The pool users are often unaware of the hazard. Children, in particular, may not realise how far out from the pool side divers can go, particularly if they are diving from springboards. Lifeguards should therefore watch diving areas very carefully for straying swimmers. The same caution applies to flumes, especially if they run out directly into a crowded pool area.

FIGURE 2-3
LIFEGUARD ON PATROL.

FIGURE 2-4
WEAK SWIMMER HOLDING ONTO POOL.

FIGURE 2-5
FIGHTING IS DANGEROUS.

ACTIVITY HAZARDS

Accidents frequently occur as a result of high spirits or seemingly innocent pool games. Some activities, provided they are closely supervised by lifeguards, can be allowed but others should be prevented.

Ducking

Ducking is potentially very dangerous as well as being very upsetting to the victim. One danger is that when water enters a person's mouth, an automatic reaction closes the airway to prevent water getting into the lungs. Sometimes breathing fails to restart when the danger is passed and the victim succumbs to what is known as dry drowning.

Fighting or bullying

Fighting and bullying are obviously both very dangerous in or near a swimming pool. Both can result in injury and bullying is also particularly distressing for the victim. Even when fighting is playful, younger or smaller bystanders can be hurt (Fig. 2-5).

Running

Running is one of the most common causes of accidents, particularly where floors are wet and slippery. Other pool users may be knocked to the floor or pushed into the water and the runner may collide with fittings or equipment.

Gymnastics and acrobatics

Youngsters performing 'gymnastic' moves in the water may hit the pool side or the bottom and injure themselves. They may also crash into other pool users, injuring both parties. This is especially true if the 'gymnasts' are big and heavy and the people they collide with are smaller.

Boisterous games

Games such as 'tag' often involve thrashing about or fast swimming with sudden unpredictable changes of direction. Other pool users may find it hard to get out of the way. Sometimes games are played with a ball or some substitute and this can also be a hazard to other pool users (Fig 2-6 A and B).

FIGURE 2-6 A & B
BOISTEROUS ACTIVITY WHEN USING EQUIPMENT.

Distance swimming under water and hyperventilation

Swimmers trying to beat their own records may black out from holding their breath too long. They may surface semi-conscious and unable to swim.

Some swimmers think that rapid, repeated deep breaths will increase the oxygen content of their blood and help them spend longer underwater. This hyperventilation doesn't increase the oxygen but, by reducing blood levels of carbon dioxide, disrupts respiration and can cause swimmers to lose consciousness (there is more on hyperventilation in Chapter Six).

Lifeguards should prevent distance swimming under water and warn pool users about the dangers. The same caution also applies to pool users who repeatedly dive to the bottom of the pool to retrieve objects as part of a game or contest.

Pushing-in

Pool users should not be allowed to push one another in. It is hazardous to those being pushed and to other pool users who they may fall onto. Lifeguards should also be on the lookout for pushing-in as an example of bullying.

Bomb diving

This is where pool users leap off the pool side or from a diving board with knees gathered to the chest and their arms around them. In this position the diver has virtually no control of direction. Bomb diving is both a nuisance and a danger, particularly to other pool users who the diver may fall onto.

Other dangerous diving

Some diving activities are safe if performed by skilled people in a supervised session but are hazardous otherwise. For example, somersault entries can be dangerous because they are difficult to control. Similarly, backward dives often cause accidents because divers can't see the water as they enter and may fall onto other pool users. Another dangerous practice is diving with the arms along the sides of the body.

ACTIVITY HAZARDS—PERSONAL EQUIPMENT

Many pools allow the use of personal equipment, usually during slack periods and subject to certain rules. The way this equipment is used may present hazards. For instance, a ball being thrown very hard can cause severe facial injury and possible concussion.

Fins ('flippers') are usually used with a vigorous leg action. This can result in injury to other pool users, especially to their face or eyes.

Rubber rings and other buoyancy aids should be proper, purpose-designed items. Armbands should be the double chamber type and conform to British Standard BS57661. Some buoyancy aids have projecting metal nozzles which can cause injuries to pool users, especially to their face or eyes. Pool users sometimes dive through rubber rings and this too can lead to injuries.

Swimming goggles and face masks can be hazardous. Goggles should conform to safety standards (BS5883 of 1996) and face masks to British Sub Aqua Club standards. Untempered glass lenses can break and cause serious accidents. This can easily happen if the goggles strike the side, edge or handrail of the pool, or if someone treads on the goggles.

Many pools supply authorised play equipment. Pool users must be aware of, and abide by, any safety rules governing use of the equipment. Lifeguards must be ready to explain the safe use of the equipment and make sure the rules are observed.

FINS AND GOGGLES

Fins ('flippers'), masks and goggles should be discouraged except during controlled sessions.

CAUTION

FINS AND MASKS SHOULD ONLY BE USED IN CONTROLLED SESSIONS AND NOT ALLOWED DURING RECREATIONAL PUBLIC SESSIONS.

HIGH RISK GROUPS

ome higher risk groups may need to leave the wave machine area or move to shallowest water.

- very small children;
- elderly people;
- parents holding small children;
- timid or nervous pool users; and
- obviously weak swimmers.

ACTIVITY HAZARDS—POOL EQUIPMENT

Wave machines, slides and similar pool features are increasingly popular, especially in large leisure complex pools. Lifeguards must ensure that pool users abide by the rules governing their safe use and be on the lookout for crowding and queuing. For more information about activity equipment, refer to the publications listed on page 48.

Wave machines are fundamentally safe. However, pool users should receive adequate visual and audible warning of the waves starting. Pool users should not be allowed to dive into the waves from the pool side.

Once the wave machine has been switched off, it may take some time for the water to return to normal and lifeguards must know what the delay is at the pool where they are working.

Higher risk groups should leave the wave machine area or move to shallow water until they are accustomed to the wave motion. They may include:

- very small children;
- elderly people;
- parents holding small children;
- timid or nervous pool users; and
- obviously weak swimmers.

LIFEGUARD HAZARDS

The way lifeguards are deployed and the way they undertake their duties affects the safety of pool users. For instance, lifeguards who are badly positioned can't maintain proper observation of the pool. If their attention wanders or they don't remain alert, a potential danger can escalate into an incident and they will have failed in their prime task of accident prevention.

The way lifeguards conduct themselves has a significant effect on the way pool users behave. For instance, horseplay by lifeguards undermines their status and authority. It will also distract them from their work and may incite copycat behaviour among pool users. Trivial chatting can also distract lifeguards.

In some pools, lifeguards may maintain observation from a specially provided and carefully sited lifeguard chair (Fig. 2-7). That's fine, but unofficial or inappropriate seating may result in a limited field of view or lull lifeguards into low attentiveness. It can even put them at risk — for instance, lifeguards perched on barrier rails may slip off and injure themselves.

PHYSICAL HAZARDS

Some physical hazards arise from the pool's design and structure and others from its maintenance and equipment. Hazards associated with the pool and its building will be identified by the NOP. Lifeguards must be fully aware of these and take all reasonable steps to protect pool users.

Lifeguards can also minimise risks by maintaining all pool side equipment in good order and ensuring that it is always in the correct place. A tidy pool side is essential to safety.

Obviously, many physical hazards are associated with the particular pool where the lifeguard is working and these will be covered by the Professional (Site Specific) Module. However, others are common to most pools and will be covered by the Foundation Module. These include the general physical hazards listed below.

Entrance

The entrance to the pool from the changing area can be dangerous. Overcrowding can occur as pool users head for the water. If there is a footbath in the entrance, the floor either side may be wet and slippery.

FIGURE 2-7
LIFEGUARD AT CENTRAL OBSERVATION TOWER.

In some pools, the entrance from the changing rooms is adjacent to deep water. Lifeguards must make sure that pool users know where the shallow water is in relation to the entrance. Even if there are warning signs and a barrier, lifeguards must still be particularly vigilant as users enter the pool from the changing area and warn them about the deep water. This is especially so with small children, elderly people or people with restricted mobility.

Size of pool

Obviously, the bigger the pool the more pool users it can hold at any one time. The more people and activities, the harder it is for lifeguards to keep the whole pool under observation. More lifeguards is one solution but this solution carries its own dangers. The lifeguards may be lulled into a false sense of 'security in numbers' and allow their attention to wander in the belief that their colleagues can cover the pool adequately. This underlines the need for training in teamwork and why individual lifeguards must understand their own role in the team.

There must be a proper supervision plan with each lifeguard having a zone of responsibility. Otherwise, there is a danger that several lifeguards will be watching one area while leaving another unobserved. We will look more closely at 'zoning' later in this chapter.

Shape of pool

Most pools are rectangular but there are variations. An increasing number of leisure centre and smaller hotel pools are 'T', 'L', 'U' or kidney shaped.

These designs present particular problems. For instance, some areas of the pool may not be visible from parts of the pool side, or walls, pillars, split level pool sides and even vegetation may obstruct the lifeguard's vision.

Depth

Lifeguards must know how deep the water is in every part of the pool and advise users, especially small children, about deep water. Lifeguards must also warn users about the dangers of diving into shallow water, and rigorously enforce diving restrictions. Signs showing depth should follow the Safety Signs and Signals Regulations 1996.

Pool shelving

Shelving from shallow to deep water can cause problems because pool users may not expect a sudden change of depth. Lifeguards must be fully aware of the problem, and especially of the dangers of the sudden drops built into some pools.

Pool troughs, gutters and handrails

Non-swimmers often hold on to the guttering around the pool when venturing into deep water. Occasionally, pool users get stuck in scum troughs or behind handrails. Lifeguards must keep a close watch on these users and advise them to stay in water shallow enough for their level of ability.

Natural light

Perhaps surprisingly, too much light is more often a problem than not enough light. The design of the pool building dictates whether sunlight falls directly onto the water. If there are large windows in south-facing walls, sunlight can enter at an angle and be reflected by the water. The movement of the water scatters the reflected light in all directions and makes the surface appear almost opaque (Fig. 2-8). This means it will be difficult (or, in the worst cases, impossible) to see the bottom of the pool or anyone under the water's surface. Lifeguards must always ensure that they can see below the surface of the water and make allowance for reflection or glare on the pool surface.

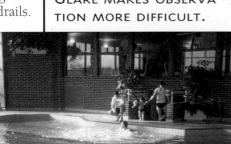

FIGURE 2-8
GLARE MAKES OBSERVATION MORE DIFFICULT.

FIGURE 2-9 A–C POOLS WITH SPECIAL FEATURES OFFER MORE CHALLENGES FOR THE LIFEGUARD.

Special features

Modern leisure centre pools often have exciting 'fun' features for pool users. These include:

- flumes, chutes and slides;
- wave-making machines and beach areas;
- diving facilities;
- inflatables, mats, rafts and other floating play equipment; and
- water features such as water jets, rivers, waterfalls and so on (Figs. 2-9 A–C).

These features are safe if the rules are followed but there are a few hazards, particularly ones relating to the depth of water, increased noise levels and restricted visibility below the equipment.

Drain covers

Diving to grab objects from drain covers on the bottom of the pool can be very dangerous, especially if fingers become trapped (Fig. 2-10). This activity should be prevented but if lifeguards see pool users diving near drain covers (or outlets), they should keep a close watch and make sure the user returns safely to the surface.

Swimming lane lines

If lane lines are left in place during open public sessions, weak swimmers (and even non-swimmers) may use them to venture into deep water (Fig. 2-11). Lifeguards should be on the look out for this danger.

Another danger of lane lines left out during public sessions is that pool users may sit on them and pull them under the water. When released, the lines can spring back to the surface which, at best, can be disconcerting to other pool users and in some cases can lead to injury.

Steps

Lifeguards must check regularly that the steps from the pool side into the water are secure and in good condition. They should discourage bathers from congregating around the steps or misusing them in any way. Lifeguards should also look out for adventurous non-swimmers using the steps into deep water to access the scum trough or the gutter. They should warn other team members if they see pool users who appear to be at risk.

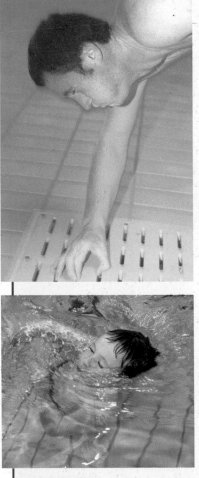

FIGURE 2-10
DIVING TO TOUCH DRAINS AT THE BOTTOM OF THE POOL IS DANGEROUS.

FIGURE 2-11
FOLLOWING LANE LINES INTO DEEP WATER CAN BE DANGEROUS.

FIGURE 2-12
ALERT OBSERVATION.

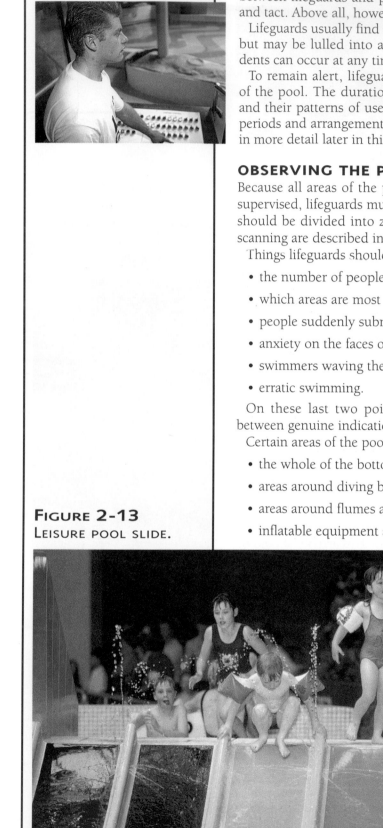

FIGURE 2-12
ALERT OBSERVATION.

FIGURE 2-13
LEISURE POOL SLIDE.

GENERAL SUPERVISION

Supervision is an essential task for lifeguards and involves direct interaction between lifeguards and pool users. So supervising a pool requires skill, vigilance, and tact. Above all, however, it requires alert observation at all times (Fig. 2-12).

Lifeguards usually find it easy to remain alert at peak times when the pool is busy but may be lulled into a false sense of security during quieter periods. But accidents can occur at any time so lifeguards must stay alert.

To remain alert, lifeguards need regular breaks from concentrated observation of the pool. The duration of duty periods varies from site to site because pools and their patterns of use vary so much. The NOP should specify maximum duty periods and arrangements for rotating staff between tasks. We will look at rotation in more detail later in this chapter.

OBSERVING THE POOL

Because all areas of the pool and its environs must be adequately observed and supervised, lifeguards must work as a team. To ensure complete coverage, the pool should be divided into zones and each zone continuously scanned. Zoning and scanning are described in detail later in this chapter.

Things lifeguards should watch for include:

- the number of people in the pool;
- which areas are most congested;
- people suddenly submerging;
- anxiety on the faces of swimmers;
- swimmers waving their arms to attract attention; and
- erratic swimming.

On these last two points, however, lifeguards must be able to differentiate between genuine indications of distress and playful behaviour.

Certain areas of the pool need especially thorough observation. These include:

- the whole of the bottom of pool;
- areas around diving boards, wave machine and other outlets;
- areas around flumes and slides (Fig. 2-13); and
- inflatable equipment and floating toys.

Observation means more than just looking. Although vision is the main sense required, smell and sound play a part too. Lifeguards should listen out for unusual sounds such as cries for help, people arguing, equipment being broken, and audible signals from other lifeguards.

The sense of smell can also reveal potential problems. For instance, the aroma of alcohol or drugs and abused solvents can warn lifeguards that certain pool users may not be fit to swim. The smell of chemicals may indicate a dangerous leakage.

Experience also contributes to effective observation. After working at a pool for some time, lifeguards will come to know the characteristic sights, sounds, patterns and rhythms and will immediately notice any break in the regular pattern.

LIFEGUARD/POOL USER RATIOS

Because pools vary so much, it is impossible to establish a fixed ratio of lifeguards to pool users. In some situations, only a single lifeguard may be on duty and observation and adherence to the NOP is even more important in such circumstances. It is essential that adequate back-up is available.

The risk assessment will determine the lifeguard cover required at specific sites and this will be incorporated into the Written Operation Procedures. Pool operators are responsible for determining the ratio.

Factors to consider when establishing lifeguard/user ratios include:

- the size and configuration of the pool;
- the number of pool users;
- ages and abilities of pool users;
- types of activity and programmes offered;
- the specific hazards at the pool; and
- the amount and type of equipment in use.

ZONING

Put simply, zoning simply means dividing a pool and its environment into notional areas, each of which is observed by a member of the lifeguard team. As well as the pool itself, zones should include access points such as steps, ladders, walkways and entrances, and the pool side.

The extent of each zone is determined by the size and shape of the pool, the activities being undertaken, the lighting and visibility, the number of pool users and the number of lifeguards.

Zones, of course, are not 'flat'; they extend down to the bottom of the pool and up the stairs to the top landing of a diving board or flume.

The diagram of a typical free-form leisure pool shows the locations where lifeguards might be stationed to observe the pool (See Fig. 2-16).

Zoning offers many advantages. Among these are that lifeguards can:

- be responsible for fewer pool users;
- be nearer to the pool users they are supervising;
- concentrate their observation on a smaller, more manageable, area;
- rotate between zones to reduce boredom and increase alertness; and
- share coverage of high risk areas with other team members.

There are a few disadvantages, however. These include the need for higher staffing levels, particularly in larger and more complex pools, and the possibility of confusion about individual patrol areas with the risk that incidents may occur on unclear boundaries. However, the latter can be minimised by the overlap of zones.

INTENSIVE ZONING

In the intensive zone system specific sections of the pool are allocated to each lifeguard patrol or position. The zones may be segments of the pool itself or relate to a specific area, activity or physical characteristic such as:

- a programmed swimming zone;
- the recreational area;
- roped off 'swimfit' or 'jogging' lanes; or
- areas around diving boards, flumes or wave machine outlets.

Intensive zones may also be linear, following, for instance, circulating water in 'river' features. Sometimes, 'rivers' go outside the main building before feeding back into another area and these need very close supervision.

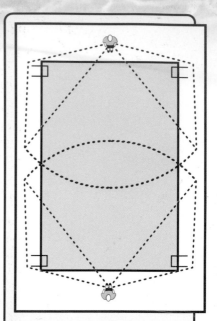

FIGURE 2-14
INTENSIVE ZONE SCAN.

The diagram illustrates typical lifeguard positions for an intensive zoning system (Fig. 2-14). Although shown within a rectangular pool area, the principles can also be applied irregular types.

Advantages

- the overlapping of zones ensures double protection for pool users in the overlap;
- lifeguard positions can be tailored to the pool users' activities or the physical features of the pool;
- lifeguards can rotate positions and thereby have a break from the most demanding areas; and
- lifeguards can be assigned to the most appropriate zone according to their experience, knowledge and skills.

Disadvantages

- the risk that, should a lifeguard fail to spot an incident, colleagues in adjacent zones will also miss it as they concentrate on their own zones;
- lifeguards may be unsure of the boundaries of their zone unless it is defined by physical features;
- confusion about which lifeguard is responsible may result if an incident occurs; and
- more lifeguards may be required with cost and staffing implications.

EXTENSIVE ZONING

Extensive zoning is more commonly found in smaller pools which accommodate a smaller number of users. Each lifeguard is responsible for scanning the entire pool area, resulting in closer teamwork (Fig. 2-15). The advantages are that fewer lifeguards are required and that the whole pool is under observation by more than one person.

However, there are drawbacks to this system. Because each lifeguard has a larger area to scan, they may not see potential incidents developing until they have become serious, and the lifeguards' attention may be unequally divided among all areas.

Advantages

- each lifeguard observes the whole pool;
- each pool user will be observed by more than one lifeguard;
- lifeguards can more readily be positioned to suit activities and positions of pool users; and
- fewer lifeguards are required.

Disadvantages

- lifeguards have less change of position and pace during their shift;
- high risk areas may get insufficient attention; and
- lifeguards may be stationed at a greater distance from pool users, increasing the risk of incidents developing unobserved.

COMBINED ZONING

In the combined zoning system, each lifeguard has responsibility for a specific area (for instance, the diving area) and also maintains an overview of the whole pool (Fig. 2-16). The combined system has the advantages of both intensive and extensive zoning.

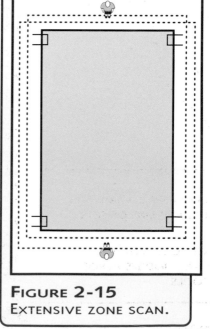

FIGURE 2-15
EXTENSIVE ZONE SCAN.

FIGURE 2-16
COMBINED ZONE SCAN

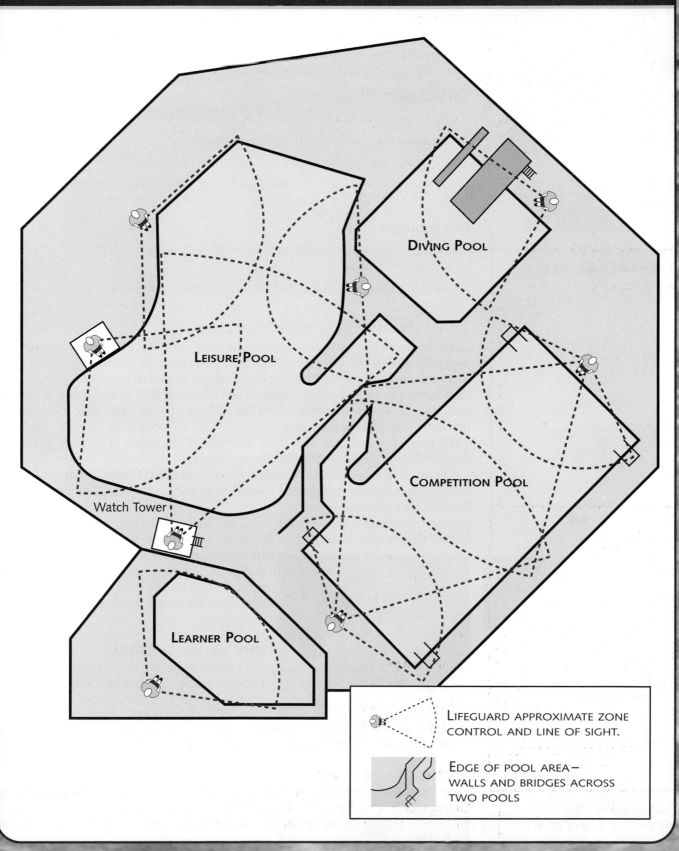

DIVING POOL

LEISURE POOL

Watch Tower

COMPETITION POOL

LEARNER POOL

LIFEGUARD APPROXIMATE ZONE CONTROL AND LINE OF SIGHT.

EDGE OF POOL AREA— WALLS AND BRIDGES ACROSS TWO POOLS

FIGURE 2-17
THE EFFECT OF FOLIAGE
AT POOLS.

The large new free-form leisure centre pools provide an ever-increasing range of features — for instance, artificial rocks and foliage, slides, flumes, 'rivers' and waves (Fig. 2-17). These can make effective observation more difficult so effective zoning and scanning is even more vital in such pools.

Many permutations are possible in combined zoning systems, depending on the type and size of the pool. For instance, in large leisure centre pools some of the lifeguards might be responsible for scanning extensive zones of clear water while other team members concentrate on smaller, high risk areas.

Advantages

- all lifeguards have an overview of all activity;
- lifeguards can more readily work as a team;
- lifeguards can identify trends and patterns in pool use; and
- in emergencies, lifeguards can contact other services (such as police, fire or ambulance) without leaving a zone entirely unsupervised.

Disadvantages

- reduced interaction with pool users to allow concentration on the whole pool; and
- the probable need for elevated observation positions.

SCANNING

Scanning, as its name implies, means constantly watching a particular zone using a sweeping action. The principle is the same irrespective of the zoning system being used and should include the whole environment as well as the pool itself.

By learning scanning skills, lifeguards can take in all that is happening in particular locations without concentrating for so long on one point that they become oblivious to the rest of the zone.

The pace of scanning is important. Drownings can occur in seconds so the less time it takes to effectively scan a zone, the better.

Effective scanning relies on both frontal and peripheral vision. Peripheral vision helps lifeguards maintain general awareness of the whole zone. Frontal vision lets them fix on a particular spot.

Some swimmers in difficulty struggle but others slip quietly below the surface (this is often termed 'quiet drowning syndrome'). So scanning must include looking through the water to the bottom of the pool as well as observing the surface. This also means lifeguards will be more aware of pool users who are diving, jumping in, or swimming underwater.

THE 10:20 SYSTEM

Lifeguards should be able to scan their area of supervision in 10 seconds and to be close enough to get to an incident within 20 seconds. This is called the 10:20 system and is one of the most effective principles for scanning a pool.

SCANNING TECHNIQUES

Lifeguards should sweep their eyes over the zone, looking to both left and right and, where appropriate, behind (Fig. 2-18). They should make a point of looking directly in front of

FIGURE 2-18
SCANNING THE POOL.

SCANNING STRATEGIES

Head counting
Lifeguards should try to count the number of people in the zone during each scan — if the number changes, they should find out why. However, this technique may not be possible if the pool is crowded.

Grouping
Lifeguards should sort swimmers into groups by age, size, risk potential, activities or combinations of the above and should monitor changes in the groups.

Mental filing
During successive sweeps, lifeguards should build up pool user profiles which include swimming ability, skill, activity, and other relevant factors. They should also notice changes in user behaviour or activity on each scan.

Profile matching
On each scan, lifeguards should measure what they see against the characteristic profiles of pool users in difficulty.

Tracking
Lifeguards should track people who submerge after diving, using a slide or flume, or any similar activity. They should also track high risk groups such as lone children, poor swimmers or non-swimmers.

FIGURE 2-19
LIFEGUARD SURVEILLANCE OF THE POOL.

their position, especially if they are on a high chair as sometimes the position of the chair can limit their view of swimmers at the bottom of the pool close to the edge.

The sweep of each scan should take in adjacent lifeguards or other team members so that any visual signals can be spotted quickly.

Lifeguards should focus on pool users and what they are doing, making eye contact whenever possible (Fig. 2-19). Pool users' faces often give early warning of a potential incidence and lifeguards should look out for signs of distress.

It is important to avoid staring fixedly at one point. Lifeguards should give their eyes a break by focusing briefly on a more distant object. They should not, however, turn their back on the zone they are scanning. If they need to move position, they should walk sideways or even backwards if that is necessary to maintain their observation of the zone.

As lifeguards come on duty, they should scan the area completely before taking over the zone. They should also note any comments made by the lifeguard they are relieving. However, lifeguards should not stop scanning when speaking to colleagues or to pool users.

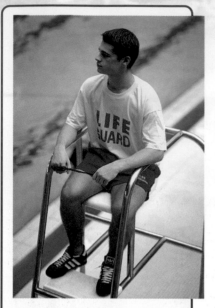

FIGURE 2-20
A HIGH CHAIR ALLOWS
A WIDER VIEW.

FIGURE 2-21
LIFEGUARD ON MOBILE
PATROL.

LIFEGUARD POSITIONS

Lifeguards may either move about the pool (patrolling) or observe from a fixed position. Both have advantages and drawbacks according to factors such as the size and type of the pool, the activities and features, and the number of pool users.

In both cases, bearing is important. If lifeguards perch on a safety rail, slouch in a chair or wander about looking bored and inattentive, it will create a very bad impression. Lifeguards who keep a sharp lookout will stay alert and enjoy their work more.

FIXED POSITIONS AND CHAIRS

Fixed positions will be clearly set out in the Written Operating Procedures. The most common example of a fixed position is the special elevated lifeguard chair (Fig. 2-20).

To allow lifeguards to scan the pool effectively while sitting down, the chair should be elevated to a height of about 2 metres (6 feet). This height gives a wide field of view and often overcomes the problem of reflection and glare from the surface of the pool. The high position also helps the lifeguard to see the bottom of the pool clearly even in deep water. An elevated chair also distances lifeguards from noise, splashing and other distractions and helps pool users to locate lifeguards quickly and easily.

The disadvantages of an elevated chair are that lifeguards are more remote from pool users. Sitting can lead to stiffness and also reduce concentration, particularly if the pool environment is very hot. There is also a risk that lifeguards could be injured if they descend from the chair quickly to respond to an incident. Occasionally, chairs are positioned so that the view of the surface immediately in front is obstructed or so that the lifeguard cannot see the bottom of the pool. In these cases, additional observation must be provided so that the blind spots are covered.

Pool staff not only need to be alert, they must be seen to be alert. Lifeguards on chairs may be watching the pool very carefully despite their comfortable position but some pool users may think they are drowsing.

PATROLLING

Lifeguards often move about to patrol the pool, rather than remain in a fixed position (Fig. 2-21). However, the range of the patrol must be clearly defined in the Written Operating Procedures and this defined range must not be exceeded.

The patrol must be conducted in a way that lets the lifeguard maintain observation of the pool at all times. Patrolling lifeguards should never turn their backs to the water. The whole patrol range should be covered continuously to ensure full observation and gain the most advantage. Stepping back from the edge will allow the lifeguard a very wide field of view. Lifeguards should also glance behind frequently so that surveillance is as comprehensive as possible.

Patrolling has several advantages. Lifeguards may find it easier to keep in contact with pool users and prevent accidents if they are patrolling rather than being in a fixed position. Patrolling lifeguards can move quickly to deal with problems or offer assistance to colleagues while still maintaining a view of their zone. Observation while moving around the pool side makes best use of both frontal and peripheral vision. Keeping on the move not only creates changing viewpoints but reassures pool users that the lifeguards are alert.

Patrolling can allow lifeguards closer observation of the pool edge and down to the bottom of the pool, areas that may be missed from a fixed position. It is important that lifeguards patrolling around the pool keep a close watch on activities and occurrences going on behind them.

There are a few drawbacks, however. Lifeguards on patrol often get wet, especially if the pool is very busy, and if this results in discomfort or chill they may lose concentration. Lengthy periods on foot can be tiring and this, too, can lead to reduced efficiency. Regular relief and a change of view is strongly recommended and should be provided for in the Written Operating Procedures.

COMBINING FIXED AND MOBILE POSITIONS

A combination of patrolling and fixed position coverage relies on sufficient lifeguards being available. A major advantage of the combination is that several observation techniques can be used simultaneously. For example, a lifeguard stationed in a high observation chair may maintain extensive observation while colleagues on the pool side can supervise specific zones, equipment or activities (Fig. 2-22). The combination also aids effective rotation of staff and interaction between team members.

Rotation of duty between lifeguards in fixed positions and those who are patrolling the pool side will aid alertness and relieve the fatigue of lengthy periods of sitting or standing. Rotation, which should be part of the Normal Operating Procedure, is covered in more detail below.

In an emergency, too, the combination has advantages. Central control can be exercised from the elevated lifeguard chair position while other team members can move about to deal with specific aspects of the incident.

In smaller pools with limited staff, lifeguards can alternate between patrolling and a fixed position during their period of duty. In these smaller pools, the fixed position should be at the deep end so that the lifeguard intensively scans the deep water while extensively scanning the rest of the pool.

FIGURE 2-22
LIFEGUARD ON PATROL AT DIVING BOARD.

ROTATION OF DUTIES

Rotation of tasks and lengths of duty periods have a direct effect on vigilance. Lifeguarding requires a high degree of concentration but lifeguards may find it difficult to maintain high levels of attentiveness for prolonged periods. So rotation between duties and breaks away from the pool side are vital, regardless of whether the pool is busy or quiet.

The Normal Operating Procedures should allow lifeguards a regular change of duties and positions around the pool. The NOP should also set down the maximum period that a lifeguard should spend on continuous duty at the pool side.

Rotation allows all the team members to work in both the easier and the more demanding locations. This helps relieve boredom, particularly during quieter periods.

In leisure centre pools, lifeguards may have to work at elevated locations such as the top of flumes or slides. They may find these duties very tiring, especially in hot weather, and pool operators must ensure lifeguards do not become dehydrated.

Methods of rotation vary depending on the size and type of pool, the number of pool users and the type of activities on offer. The period of rotation will also vary from pool to pool but RLSS UK recommends the maximum time for a lifeguard to be on pool side duty should not exceed 90 minutes.

Rotation may take place at a pre-determined time or on the directions of the supervising lifeguard. Lifeguards in high risk or wet areas (for instance, flume and slide splashdown points) should be relieved first and breaks from the pool side should be part of the rotation pattern.

Lifeguards on duty should never leave the pool side unless replaced by a competent team member. Doing so may constitute misconduct and neglect and result in disciplinary action.

When staff change places, they must maintain continuous supervision of the pool. Although the changeover allows staff to exchange information, they must remain vigilant and avoid being drawn into prolonged conversation. Casual chats often mean that the pool is not being properly supervised.

COMMUNICATING WITH POOL USERS

Supervising a swimming pool to ensure safety means communicating with pool users. Good communication between the lifeguards and pool users is vital. It enables order to be kept, the right atmosphere to be created and good public relations to be maintained (Fig. 2-23).

FIGURE 2-23
TALKING TO POOL USERS.

Although hand or whistle signals have a part to play, a lifeguard's most important communication medium is the spoken word backed up by the appropriate body language. A whistle can attract attention and will usually be followed by oral instructions although lifeguards should only use whistles when it is really necessary. Similarly, hand signals (which need to be made clearly and unambiguously) usually need to be amplified by spoken explanation.

Body language is also a powerful communication medium. A lifeguard's posture, appearance, facial expressions and gestures will all affect pool users' reactions. A manner that is friendly, firm and professional is most likely to get the most positive response.

Creating a good atmosphere may simply involve a smile or greeting when a pool user enters. Equally, a straightforward friendly explanation of safety rules or the use of pool equipment will help to build a bond of trust.

Of course, contact between lifeguards and pool users is not restricted to directive or disciplinary communication; friendly informal interchange creates a pleasant environment for both parties. It also lays the foundation for co-operation, particularly should an emergency arise.

DISCIPLINE

Sometimes pool users want to do things which could compromise safety or interfere with the enjoyment of others. In such cases, they may take a hostile view of any intervention. So lifeguards need to be good 'people managers', able to quietly, tactfully but firmly ensure that safety rules are followed and good order maintained at all times (Fig. 2-24).

If there is a potential discipline problem, the following points will help to avoid confrontation developing. Lifeguards should:

• smile and appear approachable;
• establish eye contact;

FIGURE 2-24
DEALING WITH PROBLEMS.

- be courteous but firm;
- give reasons for any warning or instruction;
- avoid anger or inappropriate language;
- never try to intimidate pool users; and
- above all, always remain calm and in control.

As well as the points above, there are other techniques that can be employed to ease tension and avoid confrontation.

Any communication should be a two-way process so listening is important. Some people seem unable to listen to what is being said to them, preferring to dive in with explanations or opinions which are not relevant to the issue the other person has raised.

Lifeguards should always try to put themselves in the pool user's position and try to understand their feelings. If there is a problem, lifeguards should ask for a clear explanation. If a pool user is anxious, confused or has a grievance, it is essential that the lifeguard knows exactly what is wrong.

Don't be frightened to admit that you are mistaken or don't know the answer to a query.

DEALING WITH COMPLAINTS

Lifeguards must never assume that any pool user who complains is just being awkward. The vast majority of people are not awkward for the sake of it. Assume that complaints have a firm basis — even if they turn out not to have, the complainant probably made them in good faith. Give complainants the benefit of the doubt until you have heard their full story. In dealing with complaints, lifeguards should be open, sympathetic and should follow the general points below.

- Listen carefully and get the details correct. Failure to do so can escalate anger and lead to a bigger problem.

- Ask questions to get more detailed information and contribute to a possible solution.

- Sympathise with the complainant, but do not accept blame before you know all the facts.

- Don't try to justify and make excuses. Be prepared to admit when you are wrong.

- Once you have heard what has happened, explain what action you intend to take to deal with the complaint. Try to find a solution that will satisfy the pool user and your organisation.

- Where appropriate, check that any promised action is carried out.

- Remember to always be polite, positive and professional.

TYPES OF COMPLAINANT

 eople rarely complain for no reason so always treat them as though they have a valid point.

It may be useful to look out for:

Anger

Complainants are often annoyed, angry even. It is important to stay calm and establish the reason for the anger. Apologise for the specific inconvenience, act quickly and tell the complainant what you are doing. Keep the conversation on the future—what's going to happen, not what caused the problem. If possible, remove the complainant to a quiet area away from an audience, provided this doesn't compromise supervision of the pool.

The talkative complainant

Do not look bored or frustrated and never bully or shout. Be firm but polite and continually steer the conversation back to the business in hand. Use closed questions that demand short, precise answers. Remember that open questions invite long answers. Don't react by becoming overly talkative yourself.

Rudeness

Again, stay calm and don't rise to the bait. Try to ignore the rudeness or sarcasm. Remain detached and cool but do not take it to the point where you appear uninterested or too distant.

The 'expert'

Don't question or belittle the complainant's supposed 'knowledge'. Diffuse it with flattery, where appropriate, but be firm when you know you are in the right. If you can't think of the correct answer or can't refute the complainant's assertions, go and find somebody who can.

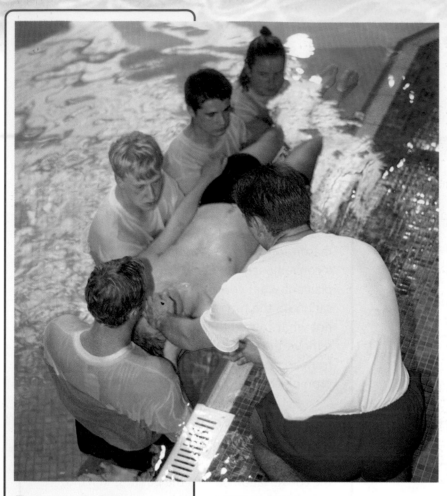

COMMUNICATION BETWEEN LIFEGUARDS

Teamwork is the key to effective lifeguarding, both in normal operations and in emergencies. Teamwork relies on communication between lifeguards — without it they can only work as individuals which is less effective (Fig. 2-25).

SPEECH

The spoken word is the most common medium for communication between lifeguards. The main problem is that pools can be noisy places so lifeguards may find it difficult to make themselves heard above the general noise. They may often need to repeat what they have said so that there is no chance of the message being misunderstood. Distance is also a factor. In modern leisure centres with large pools, lifeguards may simply be too far apart to speak to each other.

In general, lifeguards should restrict conversation to the job in hand. Idle and irrelevant chatter between lifeguards will distract their attention from observing and supervising the pool.

FIGURE 2-25
TEAMWORK RELIES ON COMMUNICATION.

FIGURE 2-26
USING A WHISTLE.

WHISTLES

The whistle is a key communication medium for lifeguards (Fig. 2-26). The NOP should set out how and when lifeguards use whistles.

Most pool users recognise a whistle blast as a means of attracting their attention. The whistle signal is usually followed by a spoken instruction from the lifeguard or by a hand signal. So if pool operators only allow whistles to be used in emergencies, they deprive lifeguards of a very effective communication medium. On the other hand, the whistle should not be over-used or pool users will simply learn to ignore it.

Whistles come with a variety of tones and pitches, so operators and lifeguards should choose the most appropriate type for their pool.

Although the use of whistles in lifeguarding has a long history, there are no universally accepted or 'standard' signals. The important thing is consistency at a given location. All the staff at a pool should know what a given signal means. These same signals must also be used during any training sessions. Despite the lack of standardisation, the signals listed below are very widely used and are recommended.

One short blast — call the attention of a pool user or users.

Two short blasts — call the attention of another lifeguard.

Three short blasts — indicate that a lifeguard is taking emergency action.

One long blast — call the attention of all pool users or indicate that the pool should be cleared.

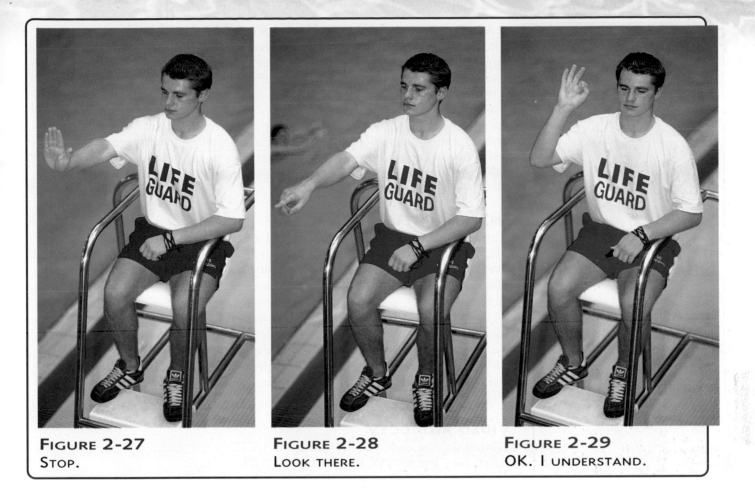

FIGURE 2-27
STOP.

FIGURE 2-28
LOOK THERE.

FIGURE 2-29
OK. I UNDERSTAND.

HAND SIGNALS

As we have already seen, distance or background noise may render speech ineffective. Hand signals can effectively convey simple messages, either to one colleague or to several team members.

As with the use of whistles there are no universally recognised standard signals. Again, however, some hand signals are widely recognised and these are listed below.

Stop (or 'stay where you are') — extend the arm forward and raise the hand, palm outward (this is like the police officers' 'stop' signal illustrated in the Highway Code). (Fig. 2-27)

Look there — extend the arm and point with the index finger (this signal can be used to indicate something to either a pool user or to another team member). (Fig. 2-28)

Call attention — raise the arm straight up above the head and extend the hand and fingers (this signal can be used to attract the attention of another team member).

OK (or 'I understand') — extend the arm sideways, the forearm crooked upwards from the elbow, and touch the index finger to the thumb to form a circle. (Fig. 2-29)

FIGURE 2-30
USING A RADIO.

RADIO TRANSCEIVERS ('WALKIE-TALKIES')

The use of portable two way radios is becoming more widespread, especially in larger leisure centres. Radios can be very useful, especially as they are not limited to line-of-sight and they can be used even if there is a lot of noise (Fig. 2-30).

However, radio transceivers suffer from some disadvantages too. They are fairly expensive, some are either bulky or awkward to carry, and all can suffer from interference. Like most electronic equipment, they are susceptible to very damp conditions and are seldom waterproof although a few can be supplied in waterproof versions.

If a pool operator supplies radios, their use must be covered by the NOP. Lifeguards must be fully trained in using the radios and must never come to rely on them as a sole means of communication.

INTERNAL TELEPHONES

Although telephones are often installed in pools, they are of limited use for lifeguard-to-lifeguard communication. It can be hard to hear what is being said over background noise and a lifeguard using a phone can be distracted from pool observation. This is especially so if the telephone is badly sited, for instance in an alcove.

Like radios, telephones are vulnerable to damp conditions and may become unreliable or fail altogether. And, although they should only be used for specific tasks, there is always a temptation for team members to use them for a chat.

If internal telephones are provided, their use should be governed by the NOP. Lifeguards should be trained to use them properly and only for essential calls (Fig. 2-31).

VIDEO AND CCTV

Video links and closed circuit television (CCTV) are installed in some swimming pools. Their use must be governed by the NOP and EAP.

Video surveillance can aid observation but should never be a substitute for trained staff. It must always be backed up by team members who are able to respond in an emergency. All staff must know how long it will take to respond to an incident revealed by video surveillance and this response time must be set out in the EAP.

AUDIBLE ALARMS

Pools often have alarm systems which convey various messages to users and staff. Lifeguards must be fully conversant with the sound and meaning of all alarms and be prepared to explain them to pool users. It is essential that all alarm systems are tested regularly by the pool operator and that staff immediately report any faults.

The use of alarms is increasing. For instance, larger pools may have alarms for fire, pool side incidents, wave machines and the end of sessions. As the number of alarms increase, so does the potential for confusion. The Safety Signs and Signals Regulations 1996 gives guidance on the use of alarms, and lifeguards should be familiar with these provisions.

Alarms calling attention to everyday pool operations should be supported by either visual or spoken explanation. For example, a wave machine alarm may be accompanied by a flashing light or illuminated sign indicating 'waves starting' or be supported by a public address announcement.

Lifeguards can educate groups of regular pool users about the alarms and the appropriate response, although for casual users this may be more difficult. One way is to stage mock 'incidents' during public sessions to demonstrate how to respond in an emergency. These must be governed by Written Operating Procedures, and adequate and appropriate forewarning is vital. Such practice can contribute to safety and also provide a positive public relations message by showing pool users how the lifeguard team can respond quickly and professionally when the need arises.

FIGURE 2-31
USING A PHONE SYSTEM
FOR EMERGENCIES.

TEST YOURSELF

1. Why is customer care important?

2. How can lifeguards raise standards of service?

3. Define a hazard.

4. How are hazards identified?

5. Name the four categories of hazard.

6. Give examples of high risk groups of pool users.

7. Who has overall responsibility for the safety of pool users?

8. Why should lifeguards discourage distance swimming underwater?

9. What groups should be asked to exercise caution when wave machines are used?

10. Describe two hazards associated with entrances to pools.

11. Which areas of the pool need especially thorough observation?

12. What factors should be considered when establishing lifeguard/user ratios?

13. Describe the advantages of zoning.

14. Explain the difference between intensive and extensive zoning.

15. What are the advantages of combined zoning?

16. What is scanning?

17. Explain the meaning of the 10:20 scanning system.

18. What height should a lifeguard chair be elevated to?

19. What governs the extent of a patrol area?

20. What are the advantages of mobile patrolling?

21. Why is it important to rotate duties?

22. How can lifeguards avoid confrontation when dealing with pool users?

23. What is the most common meaning of three short blasts on a whistle?

24. Describe the hand signal meaning 'OK' or 'I understand'.

25. What are the most common problems when using 'walkie-talkie' radios or internal telephones?

26. What events are likely to be signalled by audible alarms?

3

Supervising
Specialist Activities

Supervising Specialist Activities

CHAPTER TWO dealt with general supervision of swimming pools. Now we turn our attention to how lifeguards supervise more specialised activities and cater to the needs of special groups of pool users.

Exciting 'play' features are increasingly common in pools and they demand extra lifeguard support if safety is to be maintained. The operation of features such as diving facilities, flumes, slides, wave machines and so on must be governed by the Written Operating Procedures and the EAP

Detailed training in supervising particular equipment is part of the Professional (Site Specific) Module of the NPLQ. The Foundation Module includes general training on the wide range of equipment lifeguards may encounter.

There are several specialist publications which lifeguards should study as they read this chapter. They are published by RLSS UK, the Institute of Sport and Recreation Management (ISRM), the Amateur Swimming Association (ASA) and other bodies. Useful titles include:

- *Specially Safe* (RLSS UK)
- *The Operation of Giant Waterslides in the UK* (ISRM)
- *Diving into Swimming Pools* (ISRM)
- *The Use of Play Equipment in Swimming Pools* (ISRM)
- *Safe Supervision* (RLSS UK, ISRM, ASA, and ISTC)

DIVING

The risk of serious injury associated with diving may be very small but it is ever-present. The consequences of an accident can be extremely serious so lifeguards must carefully control all diving in accordance with the NOP (Fig. 3-1).

Lifeguards must educate pool users about the dangers of diving into shallow water and about the correct way of diving from the pool side. They must understand good diving practice and especially the importance of an adequate depth of water.

Diving accidents can be caused by many factors. These include:

- poor visibility at the point of entry;
- misuse of equipment;
- damaged equipment (particularly springboards);
- weak swimmers diving into deep water;
- divers failing to clear the area after diving; and
- diving from the side of a board.

Diving stages are often positioned over an unsegregated area of the pool. In such cases, close lifeguard supervision is needed to prevent other pool users swimming into the diving area. Some pools stop diving activity during busy periods. Others may only allow diving when a qualified diving coach is conducting programmed instruction sessions.

There are certain physical hazards associated with diving. For example, the design of the pool may not provide an adequate depth of water below a diving facility. Lifeguards obviously can't change the design of the pool, but they must be aware of the possible hazards it may cause. Diving blocks and portable platforms should only be used for competitions or when closely supervised. The use of diving equipment and facilities will be governed by the pool's NOP.

The following notes describe some common diving activities and the problems associated with them.

FIGURE 3-1
CLOSE SUPERVISION OF DIVING ACTIVITY.

Running dives from the pool side

Running across the pool side and diving in is very dangerous. It can injure the divers and other pool users they may fall onto. It is difficult to maintain control during a running dive and it is also hard for the divers to stop themselves once they've got speed up. Running divers often hit the bottom of the pool which can result in very serious injury. Even if this activity takes place in the diving area, running dives may carry the divers beyond the deep water so that they enter where it is much shallower.

Running dives from diving boards

Divers running along the board may have a fairly good view of the water below and in front of the board but not always. It depends on the dimensions of the board — on many larger firm boards, divers need to stand on the edge of the board to see the water below and to each side (Fig. 3-2).

Diving sideways

Diving sideways or at an angle from diving boards is dangerous because divers may strike the pool side. This activity (and other diving techniques requiring a high level of skill) should be restricted to properly organised controlled coaching sessions.

Sitting on diving board guard rails

Divers waiting their turn should not be allowed to sit on the guard rails of steps or platforms. They may slip or be accidentally pushed and fall onto the pool side.

Crowding on platforms

If too many pool users congregate on platforms for flumes and diving boards some may be accidentally pushed off. This danger is particularly acute when pool users are queuing on steps or stairs up to platforms (Fig. 3-3).

Diving when the pool is crowded

If the pool is crowded, it may be difficult for divers to be sure of landing in water unobstructed by other pool users. Underwater swimmers may suddenly appear in the diving area and there is a risk that other pool users could dive from the pool side into the path of the divers from the board.

Lifeguards must carefully control diving areas if the pool is crowded. The NOP may stipulate that diving must stop when a certain numbers of users are in the pool. Alternatively, staff may control access to the diving boards to ration their use.

Other diving dangers

Backward dives can cause accidents because divers can't see the water as they enter and may fall onto other pool users. It is also dangerous to dive with the arms along the sides of the body because divers may then strike their heads on the pool bottom. Somersault entries are also dangerous as they are difficult to control.

FIGURE 3-2
RUNNING DIVES AND JUMPS CAN BE VERY DANGEROUS.

FIGURE 3-3
QUEUES AT DIVING BOARD.

FIGURE 3-4
WATER SLIDES.

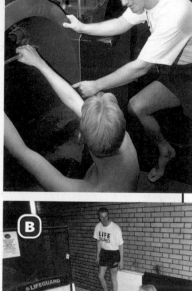

FIGURE 3-5 A & B
LIFEGUARDS STATIONED AT TOP AND BOTTOM OF A FLUME.

WATER SLIDES

Many swimming pools now have some form of water slide. These range from very basic individual slides, often found in smaller traditional rectangular pools, to the multiple slide facilities in some large leisure centres (Fig 3-4).

Slides are meant to be exciting, especially for younger pool users. They are deliberately designed so that the perceived level of danger is much higher than the actual risk.

Water slides and flumes present some of the same problems as diving stages. They may attract poor or non-swimmers, people splashing down from the slide may fall onto other pool users and accidents can occur on stairs, steps or landings.

All lifeguard team members must be fully conversant with the equipment and the provisions of the NOP governing its use. For example, they must know how long it takes to ride the slide and should control access corresponding with this time.

Staffing of slides or flumes should be determined by the pool operator following a Risk Assessment and should be stated in the NOP and EAP (Fig 3-5 A and B). Minor incidents frequently occur in splashdown areas so good communication between the top and the bottom of the slide is vital. Staff at the bottom should be aware that splashing and turbulence can impede observation.

All types of slide or flume, no matter how small , must be inspected daily to ensure that the sliding surface is undamaged and to check for wear and tear or vandalism.

In summary, it is very important that:

- there is adequate control at both the top and the bottom of slides;

- each rider has sufficient time to clear the splashdown area before another rider follows;

- observation and supervision includes steps, stairs and landings; and

- rules about the age, size and ability of riders are enforced.

WAVE MACHINES

Wave generating equipment is popular in large, modern pools. Wave machines are generally safe provided they are closely supervised and operated in accordance with the NOP (Fig. 3-6).

Supervising wave machines is part of a lifeguard's task so regular training should be provided by the pool operator. The lifeguards should know the provisions of the NOP, how long the waves take to build up to their full height and how long to subside again, and the varying depth of water leading up to 'beach' areas.

In some large pools, wave machines may have a 'surf' generating feature and this requires even closer supervision. Pool users often use body boards in the 'surf' and these should be the type made of soft expanded styrene foam.

When supervising wave machines, lifeguards should be aware of the following points:

- wave alarms may attract a sudden rush of pool users into the water (Fig. 3-7);
- pool users must be kept away from the wave chamber outlets;
- waves can cause disorientation, particularly of weaker swimmers;
- small children may be knocked over by the force of the waves;
- diving or jumping from the pool side into waves should be prohibited; and
- the turbulence of waves greatly reduces visibility through the water.

'RIVER' RIDES AND SIMILAR FEATURES

Moving water features such as such as 'lazy rivers' and flowing water circulating through canal-like basins are found in some large leisure centres. Again, these are safe provided that they are properly supervised and are governed by the NOP. Sometimes inflatables are provided for pool users to ride along the river and these will also require close supervision (Fig. 3-8).

One problem with supervising such features is that lifeguards may find it difficult to maintain unbroken observation, especially if the feature leads out of the building to return at another point. The NOP should set out the correct level of lifeguard surveillance and where lifeguards should be stationed.

In most of these features, the water is relatively shallow so even young children can stand up within their depth. However, the water is moving and small children can be overbalanced. Jumping or diving into the flow should be prohibited and lifeguards must be particularly alert when supervising flows and rivers.

FIGURE 3-6
WAVE MACHINES ARE FOUND AT SOME POOLS.

FIGURE 3-7
SUPERVISING WAVE MACHINES.

FIGURE 3-8
INFLATABLES ARE SOMETIMES USED IN RIVER FEATURES.

INFLATABLES, MATS AND FLOATING EQUIPMENT

The NOP should set out how — and where — inflatables, mats and similar floating items are used. Lifeguards must supervise such equipment carefully and be aware of the dangers of pool users getting trapped underneath it. Lifeguards should be particularly on the lookout for anyone under an inflatable (Fig. 3-9).

Larger inflatables should be positioned safely and properly tethered, usually to the pool side. Tethering must be done so as to prevent anchoring ropes from being a danger or causing injury.

Lifeguards must be positioned to have a clear view of the equipment and must be able see underneath it. They must also be positioned to easily observe the surrounding water. Certain types of inflatable may need a lifeguard stationed in the water, especially if young children are using it. Rules regarding the age, size or ability of those using the equipment should be enforced. Inflatables should not be used by mixed age groups — an adult sliding off an inflatable onto a child could result in serious injury (Fig. 3-10).

The same general cautions apply to floating mats. Although these are light, boisterous play with them can topple young children over. This can be very distressing, even in shallow water, so lifeguards must supervise the use of mats carefully.

There are recommendations to control the sizes of mats and lifeguards should be familiar with these. It is also important to follow manufacturers' guidance. Both these considerations should be reflected in the NOP which must be regularly updated to take account of new developments.

In summary, lifeguards should look out for:

- pool users becoming entangled in mooring lines;
- diving from inflatables into shallow water;
- pool users falling from inflatables who risk striking the pool side;
- untethered equipment drifting to the edge of the pool; and
- pool users, particularly children, becoming trapped below inflatables.

FIGURE 3-9
INFLATABLES NEED TO BE CLOSELY SUPERVISED.

FIGURE 3-10
PLAYING ON INFLATABLES.

SUB-AQUA

The demand for sub-aqua training time in swimming pools has increased as the sport has become more popular. Lifeguards and pool operators should be aware that special skills are required to supervise this activity and to undertaken the rescue of a diver in difficulty (Fig. 3-11).

There must be adequate coverage of any sub-aqua activity in the NOP and EAP. Pool operators are responsible for ensuring proper training for lifeguards supervising sub-aqua sessions.

For specialist lifeguards, the British Sub-Aqua Club Lifesaver Award is an appropriate qualification. BSAC is the governing body for sub-aqua sport and it actively encourages its members to gain this award so they can lifeguard their own pool sessions. However, they will also need to be trained in the pool's NOP and EAP and know the location of the telephone and first aid facilities. Pool lifeguards should liaise with the sub-aqua pool users to ensure they have this knowledge.

The various sub-aqua bodies set very high standards. BSAC, the Sub-Aqua Association and the Professional Association of Diving Instructors all provide advice and information to lifeguards and pool operators.

During pool training, sub-aqua divers use complex equipment which is potentially dangerous in the hands of those not trained in its proper use. Non-specialist lifeguards could put themselves at risk by attempting to operate unfamiliar equipment in an emergency. If a diver using an aqualung gets into difficulty in the pool, the best person to effect a rescue is another trained and equipped diver.

The same dangers don't apply to divers using mask, fins and snorkel. In this case, the non-specialist lifeguard can respond. Remove the mask and snorkel from the face as soon as possible to restore the natural airways, and treat the casualty as you would a swimmer in difficulty.

Both snorkellers and aqualung divers may occasionally suffer pressure injuries to the ears and sinuses and, even in swimming pools, aqualung divers may suffer pressure related lung injuries requiring specialist medical treatment.

FIGURE 3-11
SUB-AQUA ACTIVITY NEEDS CAREFUL SUPERVISION.

FIGURE 3-12 A & B
CANOE ACTIVITY
REQUIRES SUPERVISION.

CANOEING

Swimming pools may be used for canoe training (Figs. 3-12 A and B). This activity calls for extra vigilance and special skills from lifeguards. The British Canoe Union publish a useful leaflet *The Canoe and Swimming Pools* and BCU is always willing to offer help and advice to pool operators and staff.

Canoe training must be undertaken in accordance with the pool's Written Operating Procedures. The NOP and the EAP should set out how many canoes are allowed in the pool at one time, how the activity is supervised and how rescues will be carried out. Lifeguards must supervise the activities closely (preferably in association with an experienced canoeist) but should not unduly inhibit the enjoyment of the participants.

The activities of canoeists range from basic instruction to more advanced training and canoe sports. Each activity poses its own risks. For instance, basic programmes may take in shallow water, in which case the canoeists should wear proper head protection. Games such as canoe polo may result in collisions and there is a risk of accident from propelling the ball with paddles.

Canoeing can damage the pool and pool operators and lifeguards must supervise the activity so as to minimise this risk. For example, the bow and stern of the canoe may need protective fittings to prevent cracking tiles. If there is damage, lifeguards should immediately report it to the relevant person.

SUPERVISING COACHING SESSIONS

Pool operators must ensure that teaching and coaching sessions are fully covered by the Written Operating Procedures, especially in the case of shared pool use between programmed and unprogrammed activities. Responsibility for supervision must be clearly defined by the NOP. Lifeguards must be aware of the provisions, especially those relating to safety supervision and the ratio of pupils to coaches (Fig. 3-13).

FIGURE 3-13
COACHING SESSION.

If teachers alone are responsible for supervision involving mixed activities, they should hold the National Pool Lifeguard Qualification. In the case of programmed activities only, the appropriate qualification is RLSS UK's Rescue Test for Teachers and Coaches of Swimming.

The ratio between teachers and pupils in the water will vary depending on the activity and the specific pool. The ratios below are the recommended maximums.

- **12:1** ratio for adult and infant classes, non-swimmers or beginners.

- **20:1** ratio for improving swimmers, mixed ability groups, competent swimmers, synchronised swimming or aerobics in deep water.

- **30:1** ratio for aerobics in shallow water and for competitive swimmers.

LANE SWIMMING

Supervision of swimming lanes is essential for safety and should be set out in the NOP. Signs can be used to aid supervision (Fig. 3-14). Lifeguards must be vigilant if problems are to be avoided. Things to look out for include:

- interference with or misuse of lane lines;
- fast swimmers catching slower swimmers;
- nose-to-tail swimming;
- swimmers colliding with others moving in the opposite direction;
- crowding at the ends of the lane preventing others from turning;
- swimmers stopping to talk in lanes; and
- children or weak swimmers in inappropriate lanes.

SUPERVISING SMALL POOLS

The small swimming pools found in many hotels and small holiday complexes present specific risks not found in larger pools. Like any other pool, they should be subject to a full Risk Assessment and be governed by Written Operating Procedures.

Lifeguards must be aware of the physical characteristics, user profiles and likely activities. RLSS UK recommends that even the smallest pool should be under the direct supervision of a trained lifeguard. Some small pools, following a proper Risk Assessment, rely on other forms of surveillance. In such cases, there must be adequate provision for emergency response by trained staff.

In small pools, there may be a conflict between the needs of serious recreational swimmers and pool users who just want to splash about. Lifeguards will need tact and diplomacy to ensure that the pool is enjoyed equally by all groups of users.

FIGURE 3-14
LANE SWIM SIGN.

FIGURE 3-15
LIFEGUARDS MUST BE ESPECIALLY ALERT WHEN POOL IS CROWDED.

Overcrowding can be a problem too, especially in a small hotel pool where many guests may want to use the pool at popular times (Fig. 3-15). The number of pool users permitted must be set out in the NOP and arrangements put in place to control entry. Another risk is that the pool side may be cramped, especially if sunbeds or loungers are provided or if there are pool side refreshment facilities.

Most small swimming pools are the normal rectangular shape but some are more irregular. Lifeguards must be aware of the physical characteristics of the pool and any inherent risks. For instance, the sides of some small pools slope into a rounded bottom which can make standing difficult at certain places in the pool.

Even the smallest pools may include deep water. Signs should inform users of the depth, but lifeguards should also be ready to educate or warn users about deep water. On the other hand, the pool may not be deep enough for safe diving and the NOP will prohibit it. Lifeguards must to ensure that the diving rules are observed.

SWIMMERS WITH DISABILITIES

Of all sports, swimming is perhaps the most rewarding and accessible for people with disabilities. It provides an opportunity to enjoy mobility and a level of activity which might not be attainable on dry land. More and more people with disabilities are now enjoying swimming and many pool operators have a policy for encouraging this trend (Fig. 3-16).

Contact between pool users and operators will enable people with disabilities get the most from their time at the pool and lifeguards should help foster this. They need to be aware of the pool's policy, facilities and timetables for swimmers with disabilities.

Arrangements to make swimming an enjoyable and safe activity for people with disabilities vary from pool to pool and will be governed by the Written Operating Procedures. It is rarely possible for operators to provide individual lifeguard supervision for each swimmer with a disability but many pools organise dedicated sessions. The supervisory requirements for these sessions will be set out in the NOP.

FIGURE 3-16
PEOPLE WITH DISABILITIES ENJOY SWIMMING.

Although lifeguards can't be expected to be fully versed in all disabilities, they need a general understanding of how disabilities affect pool users. Some disabilities present obvious outward signs, such as a missing limb or the need to use a wheelchair. Others may be 'hidden', such as epilepsy which usually only shows itself intermittently.

As well as the principles of customer care described in Chapter Two, lifeguards must always remember to put people first and disability second. They should:

- treat all people equally whether disabled or not;

- never patronise but combine care with dignity;

- try not to generalise;

- ask if people want help and always speak directly to the person involved;

- speak normally;

- take care when handling wheelchairs and other equipment; and

- get on the same level as people in wheelchairs when talking to them.

SUPERVISING POOL USERS WITH DISABILITIES

The first essential is alert observation of pool users. This will enable the lifeguard to assess pool users' abilities and the potential effect of any disability (Fig. 3-17). Some people, for instance, may find walking difficult on the pool side but be very confident and competent in the water. Some people with disabilities have very unconventional swimming techniques but are excellent swimmers nonetheless. Sensitivity, awareness and close observation will help lifeguards spot the difference between competent, if unconventional, swimming and signs that someone may be getting into difficulty.

FIGURE 3-17
LIFEGUARDS CAN HELP.

Some operators provide special equipment or features (a hoist or chair, for instance) to help those with disabilities make fullest use of the pool and its facilities. Such equipment will be covered in the Written Operating Procedures and lifeguards must be trained in its use and maintenance.

Other equipment, a wheelchair for instance, may be brought to the pool by the user. Lifeguards should see that wheelchairs are always parked parallel to the pool side with the brakes on.

In some cases, special care may be needed when handling or rescuing people with disabilities. Some pool users will have weak shoulder girdles so strain must not be put on the arms or shoulders. In other cases, skin may be prone to damage or cuts calling for extra care. Blind and visually handicapped people rely on the world of sound while the deaf and those with impaired hearing rely more on visual information. Lifeguards should try to empathise and always be sensitive to peoples' needs.

In an emergency, the EAP will set out special procedures for people with disabilities and lifeguards must be familiar with its provisions. This is particularly important when there are a lot of people in the water who may require assistance in an emergency. Some rescue techniques will need to be adapted to the individual needs of the pool user and in such cases the principles of the rescue are more important than the detail. Performing an effective rescue is far more important than adhering rigidly to a specific technique.

TYPES OF DISABILITY

There are two main groups of disability. Congenital disabilities are those that people are born with, for example cerebral palsy. Acquired disabilities, as the name implies, are those that result from illness or accident during peoples' lives. The list below is not exhaustive and lifeguards can find further information in the RLSS UK book *Specially Safe*.

Amputation

Initially, amputees may have problems with buoyancy and balance but they often overcome these and become excellent swimmers.

Arthritis

Rheumatoid arthritis is inflammation of joints due to disease and osteo arthritis is the result of wear and tear of the joints. Both conditions may lead to difficulty in moving, especially on the pool side.

Asthma

This condition is becoming increasingly common, especially among children. Some attacks can be very serious and require immediate medical assistance.

Blindness

Blind and visually impaired people are often very good swimmers. However, they rely on audible warning of danger to a greater extent than sighted people.

Cerebral palsy

This condition results from lack of oxygen to the brain during or before birth. It is often severe and people with cerebral palsy may be in a wheelchair or on crutches. The three main types are:

- spastic, characterised by an inability to relax, jerking movements and breathing and speech difficulties;
- athetoird, characterised by involuntary movements, co-ordination problems, and problems with hearing, sight and speech; and
- ataxic, characterised by rolling gait, 'drunken' appearance, poor breath control and speech difficulties.

Deafness

People who are deaf or have impaired hearing rely on sight more than others. Warnings should be visual and speakers should try to ensure that the 'listener' can see their mouth.

Downs syndrome

People with Downs Syndrome are often physically well developed but have the mental age of a child. They may also have heart defects, hearing loss, visual impairment, respiratory trouble and spinal problems.

Epilepsy

There are many types of epilepsy, most characterised by seizures. People asked to help at swimming sessions should understand what form an epileptic's seizures take, how long they last, and should be on the lookout for their onset.

Learning difficulties

Severe or profound learning difficulty may also involve lack of co-ordination, poor speech and a general difficulty in understanding. People with this disability may fail to appreciate dangers or understand warnings.

Multiple sclerosis

This degenerative physical disability affects balance, hearing, speech and memory.

Muscular dystrophy

This a muscle wasting disease, leading to balance problems, poor control of legs, and chronic problems with shoulder girdle.

Stroke

The results of a stroke vary from slight paralysis on one side of the body to severe paralysis with speech and muscular control difficulties.

RLSS UK publishes a book, Specially Safe, which is essential reading for lifeguards. It is packed with useful information for anyone supervising swimmers with disabilities. It includes concise descriptions of common disabilities and covers all aspects of safety, supervision and rescue.

TEST YOURSELF

1. What are the most common dangers of diving?

2. When should diving blocks and portable platforms be used?

3. What governs the use of diving equipment and facilities?

4. Describe the specific dangers of running dives from the pool side.

5. Explain what precautions need to be taken when supervising flumes and slides.

6. What should lifeguards look out for when wave machines are in use?

7. Describe the most common hazards associated with inflatables and other floating equipment.

8. Which body governs sub-aqua sport?

9. Which body governs canoeing?

10. What ratio of teachers to pupils is recommended for adult and infant swimming lessons?

11. Which category of swimming lessons can safely be taught at a ratio of thirty pupils to one teacher?

12. What hazards are associated with lane swimming?

13. What specific factors might affect lifeguards at small pools?

14. What general principles should guide lifeguards who are supervising swimmers with disabilities?

15. Name the two main categories of disability.

4

Responding to Emergencies

Responding to Emergencies

N EMERGENCY is any dangerous situation that arises suddenly and requires swift action to minimise or avert the danger. Lifeguards must be prepared to react quickly.

Prevention is always better than cure but no matter how carefully a pool is supervised, incidents can occur and emergencies arise. Pool users can get into difficulty through ignorance of safety rules, carelessness, accident, unfamiliarity with their surroundings, over-estimating their ability or through a variety of medical conditions (Fig. 4-1).

As we have seen in Chapter One, every pool's Written Operating Procedures must include an Emergency Action Plan to cover all foreseeable emergencies. Lifeguards must be made thoroughly familiar with its provisions, and subsequent training and assessment must be undertaken to ensure all reasonable emergency action can be carried out.

The longer an emergency situation is allowed to develop, the worse it will become, so effective response calls for quick and decisive action. But the stress of an emergency can be unnerving, lead to uncertainty and cause confusion. That is why the EAP is so vitally important. It will set out:

- **what** needs doing;
- **who** should do it;
- **when** and **how** it should be done; and
- **in what order** it should be done.

Lifeguard teams won't have time to sit down and study the EAP if an emergency occurs so they must be thoroughly familiar with its provisions and be able to implement it quickly and effectively, almost automatically. This can only be achieved by regular training and practise.

The Foundation Module of the NPLQ covers the principles of implementing EAPs to ensure that lifeguards understand the range of action needed to deal with emergencies. The Professional (Site Specific) Module, together with in-service training, will give lifeguards the skills and knowledge to implement the EAP at the pool where they are working.

The general principles for responding to a typical emergency include:

- recognition of a pool user in distress or danger;
- swift initial assessment of the situation;
- response to the pool user;
- action to be taken by the lifeguard team;
- rescue equipment to be used (Fig. 4-2);
- control of the incident;
- safety of other pool users;
- safe recovery of casualties;
- performing resuscitation when necessary; and
- reporting, equipment check and debrief.

FIGURE 4-1
A SWIMMER IN DIFFICULTY.

FIGURE 4-2
RESPONDING WITH
RESCUE EQUIPMENT.

TYPES OF EMERGENCY

We can define an emergency as an unforeseen and sudden occurrence which threatens the safety or health of pool users and which calls for immediate response from the lifeguard team and other pool staff.

Some arise in the water (**aquatic emergencies**). Others occur on the pool side or in other parts of the site (**out-of-water emergencies**). They may pose little danger to pool users (**minor emergencies**) or be very serious, posing a grave threat to life or even resulting in death (**major emergencies**).

Examples of aquatic emergencies include swimmers getting into difficulties, non-swimmers getting out of their depth, and injuries sustained during activities such as diving (Fig. 4-3). Out-of-water emergencies include falls and injuries on the pool side, equipment failure, public order disturbances, fire alarms, security alerts and chemical pollution. Lifeguards should also look out for pool users who exhibit signs of medical or behavioural conditions. General vigilance, looking out for medic alert bracelets or noting relevant comments can often forestall an incident.

Regardless of whether an emergency is aquatic, out-of-water, minor or major, it will need prompt and effective action to contain the situation, minimise its effects and ensure the safety of all concerned. This action must be in accordance with the provisions of the EAP.

FIGURE 4-3
A CASUALTY IN THE
WATER.

FIGURE 4-4
THE LIFEGUARD TEAM IN ACTION.

TEAMWORK IN EMERGENCIES

As we have seen, teamwork is an essential feature of lifeguarding. This is especially true when dealing with emergencies. Individual team members can perform their roles in implementing the EAP knowing that their colleagues are on hand to support them and provide assistance if they get into danger themselves.

For example, if a lifeguard is rescuing a pool user from the water, other team members will maintain overall observation, control the public, clear the pool if necessary, help to lift the casualty from the water, assist with resuscitation and summon medical aid or other support. If the rescue involves body contact with a casualty, rapid assistance from other team members may sometimes be needed to ensure the rescuer's safety (Fig. 4-4).

In many smaller private or hotel pools there may be only one lifeguard on pool side duty. The EAP for such pools must take this into account. Single lifeguards must be able to summon immediate assistance from other staff trained in the pool's emergency procedures. Staff must be trained to assist the lifeguard as necessary and to contact the emergency services.

Although qualified pool lifeguards and support staff trained in emergency procedures are responsible for implementing the EAP and dealing with emergencies, in some circumstances members of the public can assist the team. For instance, pool users may be asked to assist by opening doors or gates, carrying equipment, helping control crowds and so on. Lifeguards should always give clear, specific instructions to such helpers. Members of the public should not be asked to do anything they have qualms about. For instance, some people become very upset at the sight of blood. Lifeguards should **never** ask members of the public to put themselves at risk.

MINOR EMERGENCIES

A minor emergency is one which, if handled properly, does not result in a life-threatening situation. However, if not dealt with promptly and effectively, a minor emergency can rapidly escalate into a major one (Fig. 4-5).

Minor emergencies are usually dealt with by the nearest lifeguard who will seek the support of other team members if necessary. In aquatic minor emergencies, it is often unnecessary to clear the pool but lifeguards should be prepared to do so if the need arises. A typical sequence of events is set out below.

1. A lifeguard spots an incident or is summoned to it.
2. The lifeguard informs other team members that he or she is responding to the incident.
3. Other lifeguards take over observation.
4. The lifeguard takes the appropriate action, which may involve calling instructions, a reaching or throwing rescue, or entering the water.
5. The lifeguard helps the casualty to an appropriate location such as the first aid area or the changing room.
6. The lifeguard completes an incident report with the pool management and returns to duty.
7. Any equipment used or supplies consumed are returned or replaced (Fig. 4-6).
8. The pool operation reverts to the Normal Operating Procedure.

This sequence of actions may take only a few minutes. But however minor the incident, it is important that an accurate record is kept.

FIGURE 4-5
LIFEGUARD WITH MINOR INCIDENT.

FIGURE 4-6
TYPICAL POOL SIDE EQUIPMENT.

FIGURE 4-7
IDENTIFY THE EMERGENCY.

FIGURE 4-8
SET OFF ALARM.

FIGURE 4-9
INITIATE THE RESCUE.

MAJOR EMERGENCIES

A major emergency is one where there is a risk of a serious injury or death. In most major emergencies, more than one member of the lifeguard team will be involved. A typical sequence of events is set out below.

1. The lifeguard identifies an emergency and raises the alarm by the appropriate means (for instance, speech, whistle, hand signal and so on; Fig. 4-7).
2. A team member operates an alarm to alert other staff and summon them to their emergency stations (Fig. 4-8).
3. Lifeguards initiate rescue, first aid or evacuation procedures as appropriate (Fig. 4-9).
4. Casualties are removed from the danger area (Fig. 4-10).
5. Team members maintain observation of vacated lifeguard positions and clear the pool if necessary.
6. Team members summon the appropriate emergency service (an ambulance, for instance) or provide any specialist equipment needed.
7. The lifeguards complete an incident report with the pool management and are either relieved or return to duty.
8. Any equipment used or supplies consumed are returned or replaced.
9. The pool operation reverts to the Normal Operating Procedure.

FIGURE 4-10
CASUALTY RESCUE.

CLEARING THE POOL

During a major emergency (either out-of-water or aquatic) it may become necessary for all pool users to clear the water. For instance, if several lifeguards are involved in rescuing a casualty, there may not be enough team members left to ensure adequate observation of other pool users.

The procedure for clearing the pool will vary from pool to pool depending on size, design, noise levels and so on (Figs. 4-11). These factors will be taken into account in the EAP and the pool must be cleared in accordance with its provisions. It is not a job to be undertaken lightly, especially at busy periods. Pool users may be reluctant to leave the water, they may become concerned, and large numbers of people on the pool side may make it more difficult to deal with the original emergency.

When clearing a pool, lifeguards must remember that the elderly, the infirm, people with disabilities and parents with small children will all need extra time to leave the water. Many pool users will only be able to get out at the steps or from very shallow water.

FIGURE 4-11
CLEARING THE POOL.

RECOGNISING CASUALTIES IN AQUATIC EMERGENCIES

Identifying the nature of an aquatic emergency is an essential skill for lifeguards. In order to take the most appropriate action, they need to recognise the characteristics of casualties. For instance, rescuing a drowning non-swimmer will require a different approach to recovering an unconscious casualty from the water.

The two most common forms of aquatic crisis are **drowning** and **distress.** In both cases, the speed with which a lifeguard notices the situation can mean the difference between life and death.

THE DROWNING NON-SWIMMER

The life expectancy of a drowning non-swimmer is usually measured in seconds rather than minutes. They often slip below the surface unnoticed.

Drowning non-swimmers only continue to struggle for a comparatively short time. It is this shorter-than-expected period which contributes to many deaths. A young child may struggle for as little as 20 seconds and an adult for under one minute. Once non-swimmers reach the drowning stage, they will be unable to assist themselves in any way, by grasping rescue equipment or a floating object for example.

A non-swimmer may get into difficulties in a number of ways. In many cases they will be in water over their heads and can be recognised by a characteristic pattern of behaviour. With their head out of the water, they take a gulp of air then sink below the surface. If they push down with their arms, they re-surface with their heads tilted back then sink again as their arms extend over their heads. They may repeat this sequence, pushing down on the water with arms extended and heads tilted back, until they are rescued or drown (Fig. 4-12 A and B).

Drowning is one of the few life-threatening situations where victims can't indicate that they are in trouble. During a typical drowning, **casualties don't call out for help.** They are in a life and death struggle and are not getting enough air to breath, let alone to shout. People who are drowning don't wave for help either. They lose voluntary control of their arms as they extend them first outwards then over their heads. However, drowning people splash a lot because of these instinctive arm movements. Untrained bystanders may fail to recognise the situation because drowning people may look as if they are playfully splashing in the water.

DISTRESSED OR WEAK SWIMMERS

Pool users who become distressed in the water can often continue to support themselves by swimming or floating, keeping their heads out of the water to breath. Distressed pool users need immediate assistant even though they may not yet be in a life-threatening situation. In many cases, panic and distress are more of a handicap than the lack of swimming ability. The casualty, although too weak to reach a point of support, is usually able to attract attention in some way, by waving or calling for example.

If lifeguards intervene at an early stage, rescue and recovery are more manageable than in the case of a drowning non-swimmer since the casualty is more likely to respond to instructions. However, progressive fatigue and panic will soon leave distressed swimmers unable to support themselves and they effectively become the same as drowning non-swimmers (Fig. 4-13 A and B).

INJURED SWIMMERS

This category includes swimmers with cramp, knocks and bumps. The characteristics of injured swimmers vary according to the nature of the injury (Fig. 4-14). Lifeguards must adapt their rescue techniques accordingly. There are specific techniques for dealing with injuries to the spinal cord and these are described in Chapter Eight.

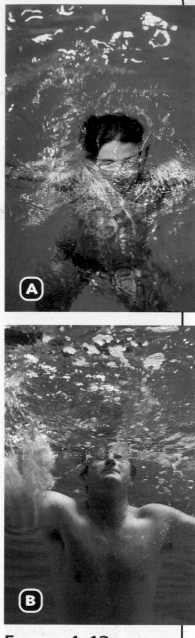

FIGURE 4-12
A CASUALTY DROWNING.
B CASUALTY SINKING BELOW THE SURFACE.

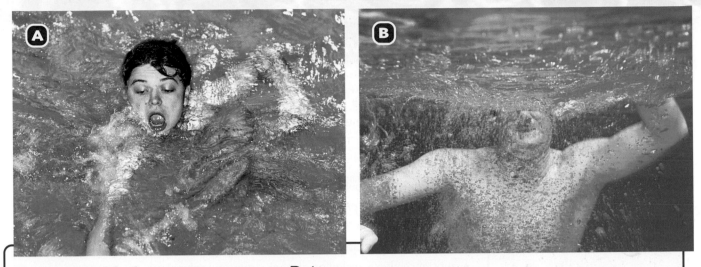

FIGURE 4-13 A A WEAK SWIMMER. B A WEAK SWIMMER UNDERWATER.

UNCONSCIOUS CASUALTIES

Unconscious casualties may be found at any point between the surface and the bottom of the pool. More often than not they are face-down. They will be totally limp in the water and obviously incapable of supporting or assisting themselves (Fig. 4-15).

The priority is to rescue them from the water or bottom of the pool, clear their airway and check for breathing and pulse. While in the water, unconscious casualties sometimes rapidly recover once the airway is cleared and adopt the behaviour of a drowning non-swimmer. Landing unconscious casualties onto the pool side after a rescue may present problems due to their limpness and dead weight.

MULTIPLE CASUALTIES

Sometimes casualties in difficulty panic and grab another swimmer, thus endangering both of them. Lifeguards should look out for two (or sometimes more) swimmers very close together showing signs of panic and distress (Fig. 4-16).

FIGURE 4-14
AN INJURED SWIMMER.

FIGURE 4-15
AN UNCONSCIOUS CASUALTY.

FIGURE 4-16
CASUALTY GRABBING A LIFEGUARD.

OUT OF WATER EMERGENCIES

hese take many forms and the EAP will set out the role of lifeguards in dealing with specific problems at the pool where they are working. Out-of-water emergencies covered by the EAP may include:

- fire;
- dangerous overcrowding;
- evacuation of the premises;
- theft, indecency and other crimes;
- assault, bullying, disorderly behaviour or similar disturbances;
- substance abuse, including alcohol, drugs and solvents;
- medical emergencies such as heart attacks;
- bomb threats and other security alerts;
- damage, failure or collapse of equipment;
- structural damage to the building; and
- chemical spills, toxic fumes or other pollution.

AFTER THE EMERGENCY

Following an incident, however minor, lifeguards will be expected to report to their supervisor or the pool operator. They may also suffer from the after effects of an emergency, especially if it has involved injuries or resulted in death.

REPORTING AND RECORDING INCIDENTS

As we have seen in Chapter One, reports are required under the Reporting of Injuries, Diseases and Dangerous Occurrences Regulations 1995 (RIDDOR). Reporting procedures vary from pool to pool but all lifeguards should understand the principles of reporting incidents. The Written Operating Procedures will detail the process at each individual pool and lifeguards will receive specific training as part of their Professional (Site Specific) Module. Lifeguards may also be expected to practise report writing as part of their in-service training.

Reports from pool operators, lifeguards and other staff have great practical value. They can be used to track trends and identify recurring problems, either of which may call for a change in policy or procedure. Reports can identify weaknesses in the pool's procedures and are an important factor when NOPs and EAPs are reviewed and updated.

Serious accidents are often investigated by outside authorities who will expect to see full written records and reports. They may also be required as evidence at inquests or court cases. As such investigations often take place long after the event, pool operators will be expected to retain records and reports.

The information contained in the report will vary depending on the type of incident and when and where it happened. Reports should include:

- details of the person making the report;
- the date and time of the incident;
- names and addresses of anyone directly concerned;
- names and addresses of any witnesses;

- witness statements where appropriate;
- some brief details of the location;
- details of any unusual conditions;
- action taken and by whom;
- injury descriptions;
- treatment undertaken; and
- details of aftercare and other follow up action.

POST TRAUMATIC STRESS DISORDER

During an incident, stress influences how lifeguards perform their duties. Stress can also have a delayed long term effect after an emergency is over. This is called Post Traumatic Stress Disorder (PTSD) and it can affect anyone who has been through a traumatic experience.

No two people react in the same way to trauma or catastrophe. Some may feel emotions such as fear, shame and anger for days, weeks or even years after an event. Others may be unable to shake off recurrent memories.

Fear can take many forms, including:

- fear of danger or injury;
- fear of breaking down or losing control;
- fear of a similar event happening again; and
- fear of being blamed.

There may be shame, too:

- shame at having been exposed as helpless;
- shame at being 'emotional' and needing others; and
- shame at not having reacted according to training.

Anger is another common reaction, and may include:

- anger at what happened; and
- anger at whoever caused or allowed it to happen.

If the incident involved death or serious injury, lifeguards may feel sadness and melancholy. They may feel guilty that they survived uninjured if other people have suffered greater loss. If lifeguards feel they could have done more, there may be a mixture of guilt and regret.

These feelings will be more intense and longer lasting if:

- someone died in the incident;
- death was sudden, violent or horrifying; or
- the lifeguard had a close relationship with the victim.

As well as these feelings, PTSD can result in tiredness, sleeplessness, nightmares, and loss of memory or concentration. Lifeguards may also suffer physical effects, including:

- dizziness and shaking;
- breathlessness or choking sensations;
- nausea or diarrhoea;
- headaches; and
- tension aches in the neck or back.

Relationships with family, friends or colleagues may be affected and sufferers may become accident-prone. Some people may smoke heavily or turn to alcohol or drugs for relief.

DEALING WITH PTSD

Remember, you are not weak if you suffer from PTSD. Nor are you alone — it is a common and entirely natural condition. Healing is also a natural process. Crying, for instance, can be very healing so never be afraid to cry.

Sometimes, however, nature can't complete the healing alone. Then it may be necessary to seek counselling or other professional help.

Some of the natural reactions that help people deal with a crisis are listed below.

Numbness

Immediately after an incident, lifeguards may feel detached and numb. The full impact of the event may take a while to sink in. It may seem unreal, a dream, something that has not really happened. Other people sometimes interpret this numbness as being 'uncaring' or mistake it for a sign of strength.

Activity

Being very active, especially helping other people, may divert the mind from dwelling on the event. However, it can also disguise the fact that the sufferer needs help.

Sharing

Do not be afraid to show emotions, talk about what happened and review the experience with others. Physical and emotional support from family, friends and colleagues is very healing. Do not reject it. Sharing the experience with people who have been through similar trauma can also help.

Facing reality

Confronting the reality of what has happened can help lifeguards come to terms with the event. This may involve things like attending funerals or returning to the scene.

WHEN TO SEEK PROFESSIONAL HELP

Sometimes the natural healing process and the support of family and friends may not be enough. The help of a trained counsellor may be appropriate. Lifeguards can get advice about contacting a professional helper from the pool operator, their supervisor or their doctor. Lifeguards should seek help if:

- they cannot handle intense feelings;
- their emotions are not settling down;
- they feel chronic tension, confusion, emptiness or exhaustion;
- they continue to have physical symptoms;
- they have nightmares or can't sleep;
- they have no-one to share their emotions with and feel the need to do so;
- their relationships suffer badly or sexual problems develop;
- they become accident-prone;
- they turn to drink or drugs; or
- their performance at work suffers.

TEST YOURSELF

1. What is an emergency?

2. What general principles govern the response to an emergency?

3. Name four categories of emergency.

4. Why is teamwork so crucial during an emergency?

5. Describe some ways in which the public can assist in an emergency.

6. Which groups of pool users need special attention when a pool is cleared?

7. Why is casualty recognition so important?

8. Name the two sorts of aquatic crisis pool users may face.

9. How quickly might a drowning non-swimmer succumb?

10. Describe the likely behaviour of a drowning non-swimmer.

11. What are the priorities in dealing with unconscious casualties?

12. What might cause swimmers in difficulty to grasp other pool users?

13. Give some examples of out-of-water emergencies.

14. What practical uses do reports have?

15. Give examples of the information which should be included in a report.

16. What is post traumatic stress disorder?

17. Describe some of the effects of post traumatic stress disorder.

18. In what circumstances should lifeguards seek professional help to deal with post traumatic stress disorder?

5

Rescue Techniques

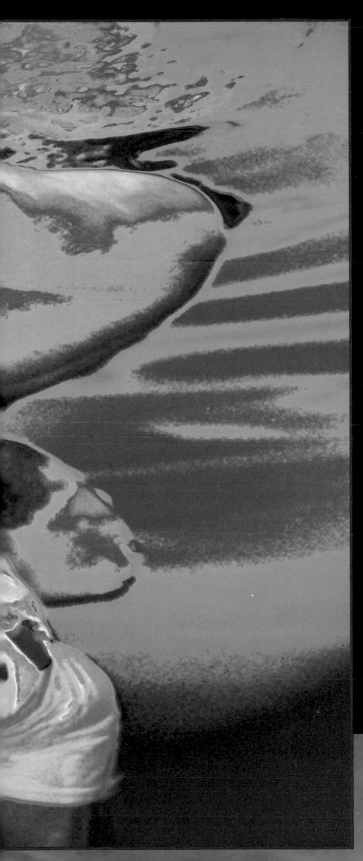

FIGURE 5-1
CONTACT RESCUE
WITH THE CASUALTY'S
HEAD ABOVE WATER.

FIGURE 5-2
RESUSCITATION WITH
TWO LIFEGUARDS.

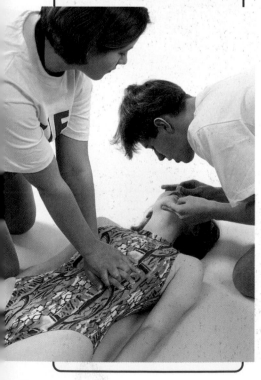

Rescue Techniques

ALTHOUGH most of a lifeguard's time on duty is devoted to accident prevention and supervision, rescue is a vital function in which there is little, if any, margin of error. The object of a rescue is to prevent injury or to save the life of a pool user in difficulty. The significant features of a rescue are:

- discovering the danger;
- alerting support from team members;
- speed of response;
- recovery of the casualty;
- administering life support or other appropriate treatment; and
- casualty aftercare.

When performing a rescue, lifeguards must be aware of the provisions of the EAP and follow them. The importance of the EAP in an emergency — and a rescue is an emergency action — cannot be emphasised too strongly.

To perform a rescue, lifeguards must be fit and have stamina. They must also be thoroughly practised in all types of rescue. This demands adequate training and exercise.

DECISION MAKING AND TEAMWORK

Dealing with any emergency is a highly stressful experience. As we saw in the last chapter, stress can affect lifeguards both during and after the rescue. A small increase in stress sometimes enhances people's performance. They feel 'sharper' and their bodies may be physically stimulated. But more severe stress can lead to mistakes. For instance, a lifeguard under stress could make the wrong decision about the best type of rescue for a particular emergency.

So a key factor is to reduce the number of decisions which have to be made. The fewer the decisions, the less room for stress-induced error. The adverse effects of stress can also be also reduced if lifeguards have rehearsed emergency action during training.

Of course, it is not only the lifeguard who will feel stress during an emergency. It will also affect the casualty, although with markedly different effects. The casualty's stress will make the rescue more difficult. So lifeguards should reduce casualties' stress by giving clear, simple instructions, by approaching quickly but calmly and by showing that they are in control.

Rescue methods are determined by the type of casualty, the nature of the incident and the physical characteristics of the pool. Lifeguards must take a flexible approach and be prepared to employ a range of skills to match the situation. For example, during a contact rescue casualties may panic if they feel unduly restrained so lifeguards should be prepared to change their technique, especially during a tow, for the sake of the casualty.

Contact rescues allow lifeguards to ensure that the casualty's airway is clear of the water, a priority with a conscious casualty in the water because a clear airway will reduce fear and panic and make the rescue easier (Fig. 5-1). If lifeguards perform contact rescues, they can rely on support from other team members.

Teamwork is important in other ways. Assistance is often required to recover a casualty from the water and resuscitation is more effective when two people work as a team (Fig. 5-2). Lifeguards must take care when lifting.

The EAP may identify a specific place — a focal point — to which all casualties and rescue, first aid or resuscitation equipment is brought and to which support staff report. A fixed focal point can save time, reduce decision making, and rescue equipment can be permanently positioned nearby.

If there is no focal point, it is important that support staff give directions to help the lifeguard bring the casualty to the best recovery point. A high chair allows a lifeguard to direct operations while retaining extensive surveillance of the pool at the same time (Fig. 5-3). Lifeguards must take care when using high chairs.

RESCUE SAFETY

Lifeguards must be well trained, highly skilled, fit and confident if they are to perform rescues safely. They must also be aware of the possibility of sustaining an injury when undertaking a rescue. Measures must be taken to minimise the likelihood of injury.

Traditional methods of escape action and release from a casualty have a place in training programmes. However, when casualties are distressed, simply providing support and keeping their face clear of the water may reduce their panic enough to mean escape action or release is not needed (Fig. 5-4).

Training for safe rescues should include:

- reassuring and communicating with casualties;
- reaching rescues with various devices;
- throwing rescues using buoyant and non-buoyant devices;
- wading rescues, especially in shallow water and leisure pools;
- entry into the water including diving and jumping;
- swimming rescues using front crawl and breast stroke;
- towing casualties using sidestroke and lifesaving backstroke;
- contact tows and tows using rescue devices;
- releases from casualties who try to grab lifeguards;
- landing casualties with help from other team members; and
- placing casualties in a position of safety.

FIGURE 5-3
A TOWER PROVIDES A FOCAL POINT.

FIGURE 5-4
SUPPORTING A CASUALTY IN THE WATER.

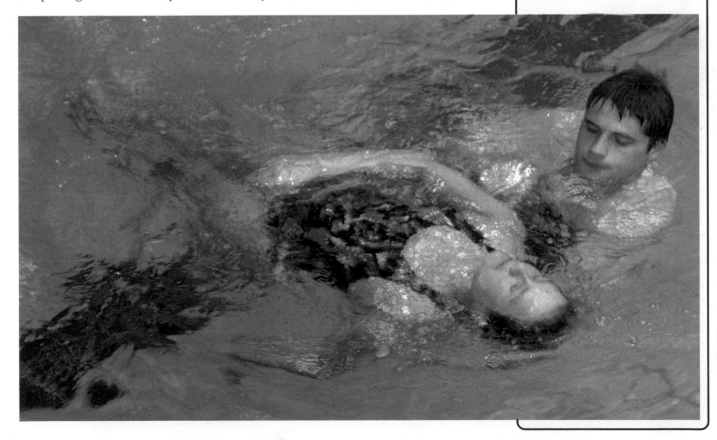

FIGURE 5-5
CALLING INSTRUCTIONS TO A CASUALTY.

FIGURE 5-6
TYPES OF RESCUE DEVICES.

LAND BASED RESCUES

SHOUT-AND-SIGNAL RESCUES

In some cases, lifeguards may be able to perform a rescue by using just their voice or hand signals. Casualties may respond to simple instructions and signals so well that they can be guided to a point of safety and then be helped out of the water. Lifeguards should use a shout-and-signal rescue when a casualty is conscious, close to the edge of the pool, and able to respond to instructions. The technique is also valuable if there are several pool users involved and the incident doesn't appear particularly serious but needs intervention by lifeguards to prevent it becoming so.

A typical sequence might be:

* attract the attention of the casualty by shouting and signalling (Fig. 5-5);
* give clear instructions;
* use hand signals to direct the casualty to a position of safety (usually the edge of the pool in shallow water); and
* assist the casualty to leave the pool safely if necessary.

USING RESCUE EQUIPMENT FROM THE POOL SIDE

All pools should be equipped with some basic pool side rescue equipment. It is bad practice for a lifeguard to enter the water every time there is an incident, however minor. Frequently, a simple rescue can be performed using a short reaching device or by throwing a buoyant rescue device to a pool user in difficulty.

At one time, pools were equipped with lifebuoys. These have been superseded by more modern rescue devices and lifebuoys are no longer considered suitable for use in pools during emergencies. They are often heavy and made of hard or rigid material. If thrown in a crowded pool, lifebuoys can injure the casualty or other pool users.

A variety of rescue equipment may be available on the pool side, including:

* fixed or telescopic reaching poles;
* torpedo buoys (preferably of the flexible type without metal fastenings);
* throwbags (either wall-mounted or carried by lifeguards);
* buoyant throwing devices; and
* throwing ropes.

Pool operators must assess how many and what type of rescue devices are needed for their particular pool (Fig. 5-6). They should consider any previous incidents and the advantages and disadvantages of each particular device.

Lifeguards must be trained when and how to use the rescue devices. Equally, they must know when *not* to use them, especially where a contact rescue is likely to prove more effective. Lifeguards may encounter many different devices at different pools so training should include as many types as possible. Such equipment must also be properly maintained.

Guidelines on the use of pool rescue equipment are published by ISRM and RLSS UK. These cover the general principles and guidelines set out in the Provision and Use of Work Equipment 1992 Regulations.

FIGURE 5-7
A REACHING RESCUE WITH
A POLE.

FIGURE 5-8
PERFORMING A REACHING
RESCUE WITH A TORPEDO
BUOY.

REACHING RESCUES

Reaching rescues are highly effective and safe because the lifeguard remains on the pool side (Fig. 5-7). They should be used whenever it is possible to conduct a land based rescue, especially when the casualty is close to the edge of the pool. Reaching rescues can be performed with various items, including rescue poles and torpedo buoys. A typical sequence might be:

- establish a firm anchorage on the pool side;
- maintain a firm grip on the rescue device then reach out with it;
- instruct the casualty to take hold of the rescue device;
- when the casualty has a firm grip, tow them to a position of safety; and
- help the casualty out of the water.

It is not usually necessary to stretch out flat on the pool side when performing a reaching rescue. However, this may be necessary if the casualty is at the limits of reach or the lifeguard could be pulled into the water (Fig. 5-8 A).

If the casualty fails to grasp a rigid device such as a pole, try to hook it under the casualty's armpit to provide support.

When using a torpedo buoy, push it directly towards the casualty while keeping hold of the strap to pull the casualty to a position of safety (Fig.5-8 B).

FIGURE 5-9
A USING THE THROW BAG.
B THE THROW BAG SHOULD REACH THE CASUALTY.

FIGURE 5-10
THROWING A TORPEDO BUOY TO THE CASUALTY.

THROWING RESCUES

With the wide range of throwing rescue devices, lifeguards can carry out land-based rescues from a considerable distance. Even in the largest pool or lido, a throw rescue may be successful.

The throwbag is an efficient and simple item of rescue equipment and consists of a length of line housed in a pouch or bag.

To use a throwbag, open the mouth of the bag wide and hold the loop of the rope in one hand. Hold the neck of the bag with the throwing hand. Stand back from the edge of the pool and throw the bag under-arm, keeping the throwing arm straight. Under-arm is the recommended technique but over-arm or round-arm can also be used depending on preference and skill. A typical sequence for a throwbag rescue might be:

- open the bag and hold the end of the rope (Fig. 5-9 A);
- throw the bag;
- aim the bag to land within reach of and in front of the casualty (Fig. 5-9 B);
- if the rope lands beyond the casualty, tell them to grab it;
- tell the casualty to hold the rope securely;
- pull the casualty carefully to a position of safety; and
- help the casualty out of the water.

If the casualty cannot grab the rope, it may be necessary to use another rescue device or, as a last resort, to enter the water.

The RLSS UK throwbag is relatively small and is easy to manage. There are larger throwbags available but the larger the bag, the more skill needed to throw it accurately. The larger throwbags should be aimed to land just beyond casualties to avoid hitting them. Practise and training are, as always, essential.

Lifeguards may also use a soft buoyant device, such as a torpedo buoy, for a throw rescue (Fig. 5-10). The sequence of a rescue with a torpedo buoy is similar to the one outlined above. The shoulder strap may be unclipped to provide a longer range if the end is to be held. The range of the rescue will obviously depend on the length of the strap.

The torpedo buoy should be held lengthways when thrown. Lifeguards should try various methods of throwing the torpedo buoy and decide which is the best method for them. Ensure any loose straps do not become entangled on pool side equipment.

WADING RESCUES

If a reaching or throwing rescue has been unsuccessful, lifeguards may have to enter the water. In shallow free-form leisure pools, this will often mean a wading rescue. Lifeguards should enter the water safely as near to the casualty as possible. As we have seen, lifeguards must be aware of the various depths at all points of their pool. They must also know at what depth they become too buoyant to perform a wading rescue safely. This will, of course, depend on how tall they are (Fig. 5-11).

In many cases, lifeguards will perform a hand-to-hand rescue but often a buoyant rescue device, or even a rigid pole, will be useful.

Lifeguards should wade to no more than waist depth so that they are not overbalanced by the buoyancy of the water. They can then safely make hand-to-hand contact, throw a buoyant rescue device or reach with a rigid one. Once casualties have grasped the lifeguard's hand or a rescue device, they should be instructed to hold firmly while they are pulled to a position of safety.

IN-WATER RESCUES

When reaching, throwing or wading rescues are not appropriate or have proved unsuccessful, lifeguards may have to perform in-water rescues with or without rescue devices.

It is important to enter the water safely. Lifeguards must be aware of the depth at the point of entry as this will dictate what method is safe. Several ways of entering the water are described below.

Slide-in entry

Although relatively slow, the slide-in entry is probably the safest in most conditions, especially if the pool is crowded. The entry should be controlled and safe, wherever possible allowing the feet to feel for the bottom and establish a firm foothold (Fig. 5-12 A).

Step-in entry

This is useful if entering from a height. The drawback is that lifeguards may submerge and lose sight of the casualty until they resurface. A step-in entry can be dangerous in shallow water as the sudden jolt when the feet hit the bottom may cause injury (Fig. 5-12 B).

FIGURE 5-11
A WADING RESCUE IN THE WAVE POOL.

FIGURE 5-12
A SLIDE-IN ENTRY.
B STEP-IN ENTRY.

FIGURE 5-13
A STRADDLE ENTRY.
B STRADDLE ENTRY WITH TORPEDO BUOY.

Straddle entry

This is a more specialised technique which allows the lifeguard to keep the casualty in sight (Fig. 5-13 A). It is relatively slow and may not be appropriate in a very crowded pool. The straddle entry can only be effectively used from a height of less than one metre above the water.

A straddle entry may be also performed holding a torpedo buoy; the technique is described later in this chapter (Fig 5-13 B).

As with any entry, lifeguards should make sure the casualty is aware that someone is coming to their aid.

The key points of a straddle entry are:

- step out from a standing position, aiming for distance;
- extend one leg forward and the other backward with the knees slightly bent;
- lean slightly forward;
- extend the arms sideways and slightly forward, palms downwards;
- hold the head still and look forward;
- on entering the water, press down with the arms;
- close the legs together in a scissors action; and
- keep the head above water.

Shallow dive entry

This is the fastest means of entering the pool and reaching the casualty. One drawback is the lifeguard loses sight of the casualty during the entry. **Never shallow dive into water less than 1.5 metres deep.** Depending on the size of the lifeguard, a greater depth may be needed (Fig. 5-14).

The key points of a shallow dive are:

- stand on the side with toes curled over the edge;
- look down and forward in the direction of travel;
- bend the knees and use the arms to help forward momentum;
- push off as far as possible out over the water;
- enter with the body almost horizontal, extending the arms and legs;
- keep the head upwards between the arms, looking towards the casualty;
- keep the body straight and streamlined; and
- after entry, raise the head, resurface and start swimming to the casualty.

Lifeguards should make sure the casualty knows they are coming as soon as they resurface from the shallow dive. They should try to skim across the water because the casualty may lose sight of them if they dip below the surface.

Follow the diving safety rules at all times, obey 'No Diving' signs, and check the water depth. Never dive into shallow water or where it is not possible to see the bottom, for example in the turbulent water found in a wave area.

SAFE ENTRY

- Make sure it is safe to jump.
- Check the depth.
- Jumps should be carefully controlled.
- Watch out for pool users when jumping.

FIGURE 5-14 A SHALLOW DIVE.

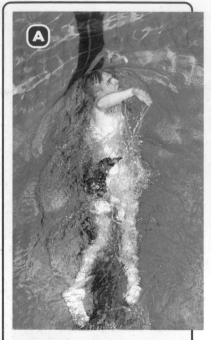

FIGURE 5-15
A FRONT CRAWL.
B BREAST STROKE.

FIGURE 5-16 A & B
LIFESAVING BACK STROKE.

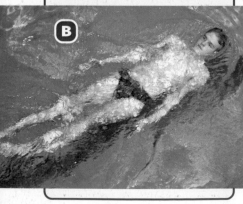

SWIMMING STROKES

Lifeguards should be sufficiently competent in the front crawl (Fig. 5-15 A) and breast stroke (Fig. 5-15 B) before starting their NPLQ training. Guides to these two basic strokes are published by RLSS UK, the Amateur Swimming Association and the Swimming Teachers' Association so they are not described again here. We shall instead concentrate on the two rescue swimming strokes, the lifesaving backstroke and the sidestroke.

LIFESAVING BACKSTROKE

The lifesaving backstroke uses a simultaneous and symmetrical arm and leg action. The main elements of the stroke can be seen in the illustrations (Fig. 5-16 A & B).

Body position

Stretch out on the back in a streamlined position with both ears in the water. Keep the hips close to, but slightly below, the surface. Adjust the body position by tilting the head.

Leg action

Variations on the inverted breaststroke leg kick are usually recommended in lifesaving backstroke but the egg beater kick is also used sometimes.

Fully extend the legs during the glide phase with the toes pointed. Recover the legs by bending at the knees. Avoid bending at the hips as this will cause them to drop and so increase resistance. As the feet drop following the bending of the knees, spread the knees and feet slightly and curl the toes toward the shins.

When the bend of the knees reaches about ninety degrees, turn the feet outwards keeping the ankles dorcel-flexed (toes drawn up toward the shin); this position is essential if the kick is to be effective.

Start the kick by thrusting the feet apart, the heels tracing a circular pattern as they travel backwards. Bring the feet together as the legs straighten. Water pressure should be felt on the inside and soles of the feet during the kick. The feet should accelerate smoothly and together, reaching maximum speed only in the final stage of the kick.

Knee extension provides the speed and so the knees should not complete their extension until the feet are coming together at the end of the kick.

Arm action

Adopt a streamlined position with the arms fully extended along the sides, hands close to thighs. Draw the hands simultaneously to the shoulders, keeping them below the surface, by bending the arms at the elbows and keeping the hands close to the body. Push the hands sideways with the palms facing backwards.

Perform a strong sweep with the elbows pointing downwards to prevent the hands slipping through the water. As the hands pass the shoulders, straighten the arms and push strongly towards the thighs.

Alternatively, a short sculling action may be used. When supporting a casualty, it usually won't be possible to use both arms so lifeguards should practise using one arm only for the stroke.

Breathing

Keep the face clear of the water. Breathe in as the legs and arms recover, breathe out as the kick is completed.

Timing

The sequence of the stroke is:

1 glide; 2 breathe; 3 pull and kick together; 4 glide.

From the glide position, the arms and legs should recover at the same time. The propulsive arm and leg actions should also occur simultaneously. Glide between strokes to optimise the propulsive phase.

Vision

When towing a casualty, lifeguards will need to turn their head every few seconds to check the direction of travel. Lifesaving backstroke allows full observation of the casualty at all times.

SIDESTROKE

The sidestroke may be performed on either side using an orthodox or inverted scissors kick. Swimming ability and conditions will dictate whether orthodox or inverted scissors kick is more appropriate for a given rescue. The main elements of the stroke can be seen in the illustrations on the right (Fig. 5-17 A and B).

Body position

Stretch the body out on the side in a relaxed and streamlined position and remain as horizontal as possible. Rest one side of the head in the water.

Leg action

The four phases of the scissors kick are bend, open, kick and glide. Recover the legs simultaneously in a relaxed manner by bending at the hips and knees with the legs and feet together. Open the legs horizontally by moving the upper leg forward and the lower leg backwards. Keep the ankle of the top leg dorcel-flexed (toes drawn up toward the shins) and the ankles of the lower leg with the toes pointed.

Open the legs wide, kick backwards and bring the feet together. Water pressure should be felt on the inside and soles of the feet during the kick. Hold the legs together with toes pointed for a short glide.

When the top leg is moved forward, it is an orthodox scissors kick but when the bottom leg is moved forward, it is an inverted scissors kick.

Arm action

Extend the lower arm just below the surface and beyond the head during the glide phase of the stroke. Extend the upper arm along the side of the body with the hand just below the surface.

The lowermost arm sweeps backwards along a curved path, the elbow bending progressively until the hand is level with the shoulders and the elbow bent at ninety degrees. Pass the hand close to the chin with the wrist bent back so that the hand can push forward to the glide position with minimum resistance.

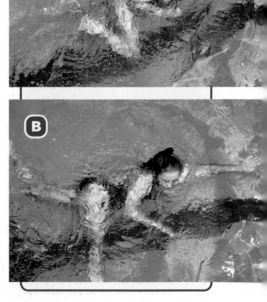

FIGURE 5-17 A & B
SIDESTROKE.

FIGURE 5-18
TREADING WATER.

FIGURE 5-19
EGG BEATER KICK.

FIGURE 5-20
FEET FIRST SURFACE DIVE.

With the uppermost arm, move the hand from the thigh to a position just below the chin, keeping it close to the body to minimise resistance. Push the hand strongly to the thigh to assist propulsion. Keep the arm extended at the thigh for the glide.

When towing a casualty during a rescue, the uppermost arm will be usually be supporting the casualty, so only the lowermost arm will be effective during the propulsive phase.

Breathing
Breathing in should take place during the out sweep of the bottom arm. If necessary, the head may turn slightly face upward. Keep the mouth clear of the water.

Timing
The sequence of the stroke is:
   1 glide; 2 pull; 3 breathe; 4 kick; 5 glide.

Vision
Hold the head slightly above the water, turning to observe the casualty during a towing rescue.

TREADING WATER
All lifeguards must be able to tread water (Fig. 5-18). With the body vertical in the water, use one of the following leg actions:
- breaststroke kick;
- scissors kick;
- cycling action; or
- egg beater kick.

The egg beater kick is especially effective when treading water (Fig. 5-19). It is one of the most efficient methods of raising the head high out of the water and is therefore very useful when lifeguards need a clear view of the water during a rescue.
To tread water:
- sit in the water, back straight, knees apart, thighs almost parallel to the surface;
- keep your arms below the surface and use a relaxed sculling action with the hands;
- drive the legs in an alternating circular pattern, rotating at the knees;
- as one leg drives, the other recovers.

To move through the water (during a tow, for example), the leg and body positions are altered slightly so that the feet drive downward opposite to the direction of travel.

SUBMERGED RESCUES

DIVING
Lifeguards must be able to dive to the deepest part of the pool to recover a casualty lying on the bottom. They must also be able to swim underwater to recover a submerged casualty.

In Foundation Module training, the depth of the pool where training takes place will be recorded during assessment.

There are several methods of reaching the bottom of the pool, including:
- a feet-first surface dive;
- a head-first surface dive; and
- a dive from the pool side.

To recover a casualty using a feet-first surface dive, first enter the water by the safest method and swim to a point above the submerged casualty.

Tread water then use a strong breaststroke kick or egg beater kick and press downwards with the hands to raise the body vertically. Breathe in before submerging.

Keep the legs together and the hands at the sides in a streamlined position. Body weight will cause the lifeguard to sink. As the head submerges, sweep the arms upwards (Fig. 5-20).

Once the feet touch the bottom, lifeguards should 'tuck' or 'pike' the body to enable them to grasp the casualty. They should use both hands to hold the casualty under the armpits, then push off from the bottom of the pool, keeping hold of the casualty.

To recover a casualty using a head-first surface dive, first enter the water by the safest method and swim to a point directly above the submerged casualty.

Submerge the head and shoulders by pulling the arms backwards in a wide breast stroke type movement. Bend at the waist and lift the legs up out of the water (Fig. 5-21). Upon submerging, gain additional depth and manoeuvrability by swimming.

Recover the casualty as described above. Use both hands to hold the casualty under the armpits, then push off from the bottom of the pool keeping hold of the casualty.

To recover a casualty using a dive from the pool side, the water must be at least two metres deep. This is most important. Make sure there are no other pool users in the way, then take a deep breath, being careful not to hyperventilate.

Dive at an angle to reach the pool bottom then recover the casualty as described above (Fig. 5-22).

It is also possible to enter the water feet-first using a compact jump. Again, it is vital that the water is deep enough for this entry to be safe.

Lifeguards should keep their eyes open during the dives and while under water.

FIGURE 5-21
HEAD FIRST SURFACE DIVE.

FIGURE 5-22
DIVING TO THE BOTTOM OF THE POOL FROM THE POOL SIDE.

FIGURE 5-23
SUBMERGED CASUALTY.

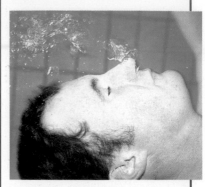

SWIMMING UNDERWATER

Lifeguards must be able to swim underwater to recover casualties. They should use a breast stroke arm and leg action (keeping the chin close to the chest and arms close to the body) or use a breaststroke arm action and front crawl kick.

The arms should be extended beyond the head to guard against submerged obstructions, especially in a free-form leisure pool.

The pressure of water increases with depth. Below 1.5 metres, it can cause pain and damage to the middle ear, ear drums and sinuses. The pressure can be equalised on the ears and sinuses by:

- holding the nose;
- exhaling through the nostrils;
- swallowing; or
- moving the jaw.

Lifeguards who are susceptible to ear, nose and throat conditions should take advice from their doctor. The condition should be recorded in their personnel files, or noted in their Log Book.

SUBMERGED CASUALTIES

Rescuing submerged casualties is an essential lifeguard skill (Fig. 5-23). During training lifeguards will use a submersible manikin or a Laerdal Resusci Junior manikin. Both of these can lie on the pool bottom.

These manikins can be recovered by grasping underneath the arms. When this skill is used on real casualties, they should be grasped under the armpits as described above. If there is a likelihood of spinal injury, the vice grip should be applied as soon as the casualty reaches the surface of the water if it hasn't already been used from the point of recovery. In very deep water, specific spinal cord injury management skills may not be practicable. There is more on spinal cord injury management in Chapter Eight.

FIGURE 5-24
RECOVERY OF CASUALTY
SUPPORTED BY TORPEDO
BUOY.

TORPEDO BUOYS IN SUBMERGED RESCUES

In some submerged rescues, it may be useful for lifeguards to dive to a casualty while holding a torpedo buoy. This will give immediate support to both casualty and lifeguard when submerged and also help on the surface when towing the casualty to a point of support (Fig. 5-24).

Lifeguards should enter the water safely with the torpedo buoy and swim to a point above the submerged casualty. Holding on to the end of the torpedo buoy harness, they should surface dive (head- or feet-first as appropriate). When the casualty is located on the pool bottom, lifeguards should raise the casualty to the surface using both hands under the casualty's armpits while keeping hold of the strap of the torpedo if the depth of water allows.

Once on the surface, lifeguards should place the torpedo buoy under the casualty and proceed to a point of support and proceed to a suitable point of support.

RELEASE AND ESCAPE METHODS

During a rescue, casualties are often panicking. They may try to grab lifeguards who come to their aid, thereby endangering both of them. Even if casualties have not shown signs of panic as the rescue begins, by the time lifeguards reach them the situation may have changed. So despite close observation and a correct initial decision about how to perform the rescue, lifeguards may still find themselves facing a very distressed and desperate casualty. Lifeguards need the necessary skills to release the grip of panicking casualties and escape from the danger they pose.

If lifeguards have a torpedo buoy, it can be used very effectively to block casualties who grab at them. The torpedo buoy will also help calm casualties because they will have something buoyant (other than the lifeguard) to hold onto.

The most common techniques a lifeguard may need are:

- escape from a rear grasp by one of two methods; and
- escape from a front grasp.

ESCAPES FROM A REAR GRASP

Lifeguards should use this escape method if they are grasped from behind around the neck (Fig. 5-25):

- take a deep breath, tuck the chin into the chest;
- grasp the casualty's elbow and wrist on the one arm;
- push up the elbow and pull down the wrist of the same arm rapidly and vigorously;
- push the casualty's arm up over the head, and duck;
- as the grasp is broken, escape behind and away from the casualty; then
- adopt a defensive stand off position and reassess the situation.

Lifeguards should use this escape method if they are grasped from behind around the waist (even if their arms are pinned) (Fig. 5-26):

- take hold of a finger or thumb of each of the casualty's hands;
- exert pressure against the joints to lever the hands apart;
- push the elbows and hands outwards, forcing the casualty's arms wide apart;
- release the hold and swim quickly out of reach; then
- adopt a defensive stand off position and reassess the situation.

ESCAPE FROM A FRONT GRASP

Lifeguards may find a panicking casualty grabs them from the front around the head, neck, chest, arms or body. They should start to escape immediately to prevent the casualty's legs wrapping around them. Lifeguards should use this escape method if they are grasped from the front (Fig. 5-27):

- take a deep breath and tuck the chin into the chest;
- extend the arms forcefully against the casualty's chest, armpits or waist;
- duck away vigorously underwater and out of reach; then
- adopt a defensive stand off position and reassess the situation.

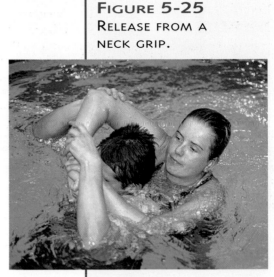

FIGURE 5-25
RELEASE FROM A NECK GRIP.

FIGURE 5-26
RELEASE FROM A BODY HOLD.

FIGURE 5-27
RELEASE FROM A FRONT GRIP.

FIGURE 5-28
TURNING THE CASUALTY TO A FACE-UP POSITION.

RESCUING UNCONSCIOUS CASUALTIES

Unlike conscious casualties who may become very distressed during a rescue, lifeguards will not face resistance when rescuing unconscious casualties. On the other hand, unconscious casualties will be unable to contribute 'self-help' to lifeguards, will give no indication about their state and will be a 'dead weight' when it comes to getting them out of the pool. They will also obviously also require medical attention (resuscitation is dealt with in Chapter Six).

Unconscious casualties are most likely to be lying face down in water. If they have not stopped breathing already, they will within seconds. Speed, care and continuous observation are essential when rescuing unconscious casualties and getting them to a place where resuscitation can be performed.

When rescuing unconscious casualties from the surface or the bottom of the pool, lifeguards may need to turn them from a face-down position to a face-up position, both to ensure an open airway and to tow them to a point of support (Fig. 5-28). To turn an unconscious casualty:

- swim to the side to the casualty;
- lift one shoulder and depress the other in order to rotate the casualty's body; then
- support the casualty's back and chin as the casualty is moved into a towing position.

Even when casualties are in standing depth water, the method of turning them is the same.

CASUALTIES WITH SPECIAL NEEDS

Rescuing casualties with suspected spinal injuries may cause extensive further damage if not handled correctly. Spinal injury management requires specialist training and assistance and is dealt with in Chapter Eight.

In Chapter Three we looked at the special needs of swimmers with disabilities. Generally, the skills used by lifeguards when rescuing pool users with disabilities are the same as for any other group but some slight variations may be necessary, depending on the casualty's needs.

Lifeguards and trainers should refer to RLSS UK's book *Specially Safe,* which contains more detailed information.

TOWING METHODS

During a rescue, lifeguards frequently have to move casualties in the water to a point of support. They usually do this by towing them. There are various ways of towing a casualty. In selecting the most appropriate method lifeguards should consider the distance to be towed, the degree of support required by the casualty and the casualty's need to feel secure and safe.

Tows used by lifeguards fall into three groups:

- head tows, where the lifeguard is holding the chin of the casualty;
- body tows, also referred to as support tows; and
- tows using rescue devices such as torpedo buoys.

Head tows provide a clear airway and allow some constraint if a casualty is panicking. But, from the casualty's point of view, body tows may be less stressful as they provide support and allow the casualty free movement of their head and arms.

In the descriptions below, we assume casualties are not using their legs or arms to assist propulsion. In many cases, they will be unable to and lifeguards must be trained and assessed on this 'worst case' assumption. However, in many actual rescues, the casualty may assist during a tow by moving their legs, arms and hands. Whenever appropriate, lifeguards should ask casualties to co-operate and assist.

EXTENDED TOW

This type of head tow is only really suitable if the casualty is passive and co-operative. It is also effective with unconscious casualties. It is essential for the sake of the casualty to ensure that the lifeguard's hand is cupped around the chin with fingers kept well clear of the throat (Fig. 5-29). To perform an extended tow:

- take hold of the casualty's chin;
- use a lifesaving backstroke kick or a sidestroke kick;
- keep the arms straight and in line with the casualty, with the elbows locked; and
- observe the casualty and watch the direction of travel.

CHIN TOW

This type of head tow is also suitable when dealing with a passive or unconscious casualty. However, with the co-operation of the casualty, it can be used in most situations. It is essential for the sake of the casualty to ensure that the lifeguard's hand is cupped around the chin with fingers kept well clear of the throat (Fig. 5-30). To perform a chin tow:

- place one hand on the casualty's chin;
- move behind the casualty's head;
- rest the casualty's head on the lifeguard's shoulder (on the same side as the towing arm);
- place the elbow of the towing arm against the casualty's shoulder;
- use a lifesaving backstroke kick or a sidestroke kick;
- maintain cheek to cheek contact with the casualty contact throughout the tow; and
- observe the casualty and watch the direction of travel.

FIGURE 5-29
EXTENDED TOW.

FIGURE 5-30
CHIN TOW.

FIGURE 5-31
ARM SUPPORT TOW.

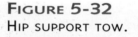

FIGURE 5-32
HIP SUPPORT TOW.

FIGURE 5-33
HIP SUPPORT TOW
(UNDERWATER).

SUPPORT TOWS (BODY TOWS)

In these tows, lifeguards grasp the casualty's body, allowing them free movement of their head and, in some cases, their arms. Support tows are particularly effective over short distances but may also be used over the longer distances in large swimming pools and lidos.

ARM SUPPORT TOW

This tow is particularly appropriate if the casualty is reasonably passive and co-operative. Ensure the casualty's head is kept above the surface. It may be possible to have the back of the casualty's head resting on the lifeguard's arm (Fig. 5-31). To perform an arm support tow:

• grasp the inside of the upper arm of the casualty;

• keep the arm straight and swim sidestroke or lifesaving backstroke; and

• observe the casualty and watch the direction of travel.

HIP SUPPORT TOW

During this tow, lifeguards sit the casualty on their hip with their arm under the casualty's arm. The hip support tow is particularly useful for smaller casualties or young children. The casualty's position on the lifeguard's hip allows control and reassures the casualty (Fig 5-32).

However, with larger, heavier casualties, the lifeguard may be intermittently underwater during the tow (Fig. 5-33). It is only practicable to tow a very short distance (less than a few metres) while underwater and the lifeguard will have less control. This tow can also be used in standing depth water.

To perform a hip support tow:

- approach the casualty from the rear;
- grasp the casualty across the chest or around the waist, depending on their size, placing the lifeguard's arm under the casualty's arm;
- grip the casualty tightly to the side;
- swim using the sidestroke kick: and
- observe the casualty and watch the direction of travel.

SHOULDER SUPPORT TOW

In this tow, the lifeguard places one shoulder under the armpit of the casualty (Fig. 5-34). This tow can also be used in standing depth water. It is therefore useful when children become distressed in relatively shallow water.

However, with larger, heavier casualties in deeper water, the lifeguard may be intermittently underwater during the tow. It is only practicable to tow a very short distance (less than a few metres) while underwater and the lifeguard will have less control.

To perform a shoulder support tow:

- approach the casualty from the rear (in some cases it may be appropriate to approach from underwater) (Fig. 5-35);
- grasp the casualty under one arm and place the hand under the casualty's armpit;
- swim using sidestroke: and
- observe the casualty and watch the direction of travel.

RESCUES WITH A TORPEDO BUOY

ENTERING THE POOL

Hold the torpedo buoy in one hand with the strap over one shoulder and enter the water using the slide-in entry described earlier. Once in the water, lifeguards should place the torpedo buoy behind them, being careful not to get tangled up in the strap.

In deeper water, the straddle entry, described earlier in this chapter, may be more appropriate (Fig. 5-36). Lifeguards should hold the torpedo buoy across the chest with the ends under the arms and the remainder of the strap held in the hands.

FIGURE 5-34
SHOULDER SUPPORT TOW.

FIGURE 5-35
SHOULDER SUPPORT TOW (UNDERWATER).

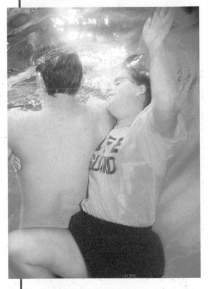

FIGURE 5-36
STRADDLE ENTRY.

FIGURE 5-37
SWIMMING WITH A TORPEDO BUOY.

FIGURE 5-38
TORPEDO BUOY RESCUE OF A CONSCIOUS CASUALTY.

FIGURE 5-39
TORPEDO BUOY RESCUE OF AN UNCONSCIOUS CASUALTY.

SWIMMING WITH A TORPEDO BUOY

Place the shoulder strap across the shoulder, and ensure that the trailing strap does not become entangled between the legs.

If the rescue involves a short swim to the casualty, the front crawl or breaststroke should be used with the torpedo buoy across the chest and under the arms (Fig. 5-37). If the rescue involves a longer swim to the casualty, lifeguards should use an appropriate stroke while towing the torpedo buoy behind with the strap over the head and across the chest.

TORPEDO BUOY RESCUES OF CONSCIOUS CASUALTIES

Swim to the casualty then move the shoulder strap over the head so that it is only over one shoulder. Reach out with the torpedo buoy, holding it firmly with both hands, and instruct the casualty to lean forward and grasp it. Hold the other end of the torpedo buoy and tow the casualty to safety. Lifeguards can use the extension of the strap to maintain a safe distance if the casualty is panicking and attempting to grab them (Fig. 5-38).

The casualty can be either on their front or back depending on which position they find most secure.

TORPEDO BUOY RESCUES OF UNCONSCIOUS CASUALTIES

The approach will usually be the same as for a conscious casualty. The unconscious casualty will usually be face down. Lifeguards should slide the torpedo buoy under the casualty's chest and clip the two ends of the buoy together across the back. The casualty can then be turned onto their back ready to be towed tow to a point of support (Fig. 5-39).

Speed, care and continuous observation are essential when rescuing unconscious casualties. They require medical attention and resuscitation and these are dealt with in Chapter Six.

LANDINGS, LIFTS AND CARRIES

Once casualties have been rescued, they will usually need to be assisted from the water (landed) and moved to a suitable position (usually on the pool side) for possible resuscitation, medical attention and recovery. The techniques described below should always be used in the context of the EAP of the pool where the rescue takes place.

Great care must be taken when moving casualties to avoid causing them injury. Casualties should only be lifted if there is no other way of getting them out of the water or of moving them. For instance, lifeguards can often land casualties without lifting in free-form leisure pools which have a 'beach' area.

When lifting, lifeguards must make sure their technique will not result in injury to themselves. They should always lift using their legs not their backs, be aware of the provisions of the Health and Safety at Work Manual Handling Operations Regulations 1992, and work with other members of the lifeguard team and support staff.

Because lifting casualties can be hazardous, it should be undertaken by at least two lifeguards whenever possible. RLSS UK does not countenance unassisted lifting during training or assessment of the Foundation Module for the NPLQ. However, in an emergency there may be only one lifeguard available. The safety of casualties is the priority and a one-person lift may be the only option.

Several factors affect how easily casualties can be lifted from the water. One is the distance between the surface of the water and the top edge of the pool, described as the freeboard. The design of pools varies greatly and the freeboard with it, ranging from deck level pools to the very high sides found in some older pools. The design of pool side troughs or rails may also make lifting more difficult.

In some cases, it may be helpful to move casualties to shallower water so that the lifeguards are standing firmly on the pool bottom when lifting.

Before casualties can be landed onto the pool side they will need to be supported in the water at the edge of the pool (Fig. 5-40). Lifeguards should establish the best point of support (such as the edge of the pool, the rail or the trough). Casualties should be fairly close to the point of support and be turned to face it, taking care not to crush their face against the edge of the pool. Lifeguards should then position their arms, one at a time, under the casualty's armpits and take a firm grip of the support. They can provide additional support by placing one knee between the casualty's thighs and resting the other leg against the side of the pool.

Lifeguards should support the casualty's head by resting it on one shoulder, taking care to keep the casualty's airway clear. This is especially important in the case of unconscious casualties.

If a lifeguard is tired after a lengthy tow, a pause to regain strength may be needed before assisting with the landing. If exhausted, the lifeguard may have to leave the entire landing process to other team members.

When approaching the edge of the pool at the end of a tow, it helps to head for the exit steps from the pool. This will enable the lifeguard, once the casualty is secure, to get out of the water safely and easily.

LANDING THE CASUALTY

Landing a casualty is often the most difficult part of a rescue. Lifeguards should summon help from other team members using the communication methods described in Chapter Two.

As noted above, lifeguards must take care not to injure either the casualty or themselves when lifting.

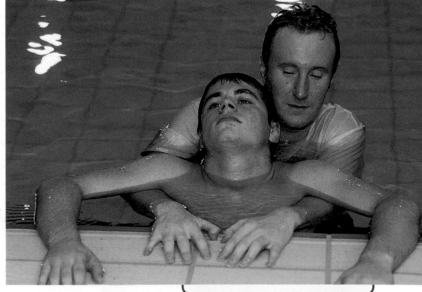

FIGURE 5-40
THE SUPPORT POSITION ON THE SIDE OF THE POOL.

Injuries are less likely if lifeguards keep themselves fit and develop strong back, stomach and leg muscles. Using the back, instead of the legs, will lead to injury sooner or later. The points below will contribute to safe lifting.

- Make a firm base with the feet, keeping them about a shoulder width apart.
- Lift with the legs, bending the knees rather than the back.
- Do not kneel or overflex the knees.
- Keep the chin held in and raised as this helps keep the back straight.
- Ensure the load is as close to the body as possible.
- Keep the arms and elbows tucked in close to the body.
- Do not twist the back but change direction by moving the feet first.

If casualties have to be landed over the edge of the pool, there is absolutely no need to 'bounce' them up and down in the water before the lift. Not only will this jeopardise control, it may also injure or distress the casualties.

During the lift, lifeguards must be careful not to bump casualties against the edge of the pool.

If the lift becomes difficult, it should be stopped, the situation reassessed, team members repositioned as necessary and a fresh attempt made. This is particularly important if a casualty is very heavy.

Do not drag casualties across the edge of the pool. Even though there should be a safe edge to the pool, joints between tiles or cracks in them can cause injury.

Pay particular attention to casualties' heads throughout the landing, particularly when casualties are lowered to the floor. The head may drop suddenly if not supported.

If casualties are conscious, move them away from the edge of the water before administering any first aid or aftercare. Unconscious casualties may require immediate resuscitation where they are landed, otherwise they should be moved away from the edge, placed in the recovery position and provided with medical support.

Various factors will affect which landing method lifeguards choose. They include:

- the strength, height, and fitness of individual lifeguards;
- the experience of the team;
- the casualty's condition, height and weight;
- whether the pool design allows a slope landing or a lift; and
- the provisions of the EAP.

In order to become competent at landing casualties, the team will need to practise all the methods and be ready to select, and possibly adapt, the most suitable one for any given situation.

GENTLE SLOPE LANDINGS

These can be used where there is a beach or shallow water area, such as those often found in free-form leisure pools (Fig. 5-41). This type of landing can take three forms:

- an assisted walk out;
- a pull ashore; and
- an assisted carry.

The assisted walk out is appropriate when casualties are exhausted but can walk with help. After allowing a casualty to rest in shallow water, lifeguards should slide their head under the casualty's armpit and place an arm round their waist. If the casualty is heavy (bearing in mind the provisions of the Manual Handling Regulations), a second lifeguard should assist from the other side of the casualty.

FIGURE 5-41
ASSIST A CASUALTY FROM THE WATER BY WALKING OUT.

A pull ashore can be used where the pool bottom slopes gently, for instance at beach areas (Fig. 5-42). It is particularly appropriate if a casualty can't provide any self-help. The lifeguard should bring the casualty to waist deep water near the edge and summon assistance from other team members. With their aid, the lifeguard should walk backwards with the back straight, supporting the casualty under the armpits and holding the wrists.

The assisted carry can be used if the casualty can't provide any self-help. It relies on support from other team members. One lifeguard should support the casualty under the armpits and take hold of the wrists while a second lifeguard takes hold of the casualty's legs and ankles. If more lifeguards are available, extra support can be given to the casualty's body.

STIRRUP LIFT

The stirrup lift can be used for steep slope landings and is appropriate when the casualty can provide some self-help (Fig. 5-43). It is often used to land casualties from a support position in the water. To perform a stirrup lift, follow the procedure below.

Move to the casualty's side or back. Reach down and cup one hand under the casualty's foot or knee, while maintaining a firm grip on the pool side with the other hand. Alternatively, it may be possible to use the thigh as a step up.

If the casualty is able to co-operate fully, cup both hands under the casualty's foot or knee, lift the casualty and instruct them to pull themselves out of the water, using clear and simple language. Support the casualty during the landing.

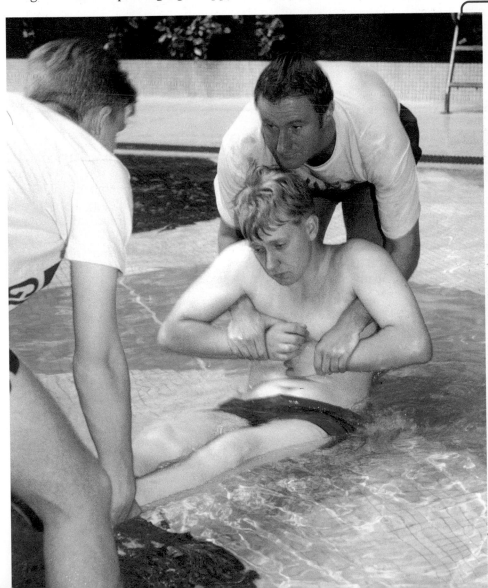

FIGURE 5-42
ASSIST A CASUALTY FROM THE WATER BY PULLING ASHORE.

FIGURE 5-43
STIRRUP LIFT.

BACK INJURIES

When lifting casualties or equipment, lifeguards must be very careful not to risk injuring their back.

The key points are:

- the hands must have a secure grip on the load;
- the feet must be placed firmly on the floor about a shoulder's width apart;
- the back should be straight throughout the lift;
- the knees should be bent in a crouching position; and
- the power of the lift should come from the legs, not the back.

In some of the illustrations, the models appear to be lifting with their backs rather than their legs. This is due to the camera angle needed to catch the action. Lifeguards must be guided by the points above, NOT by the distortion of the illustrations.

FIGURE 5-44 STRAIGHT ARM LIFT.

THE ASSISTED LIFT

1. Keep the casualty facing the pool side. The first stage is to raise the casualty's hands to the pool side, their wrists held firmly by team members. In some cases, they can hold both the wrist and arm, allowing more control.

2. On an agreed command, the team should all lift the casualty at the same time. Team members on the pool side should lift the casualty out of the water until the hips or thighs are level with the top of the pool edge. They should then bend the casualty at the waist and lower the trunk to the floor, keeping both trunk and head well supported. The casualty's legs can then be lifted out of the water, maintaining support. Both legs can usually be lifted together but in the case of heavy casualties, one leg at a time may be safer.

3. One of the lifeguards should take care of the casualty's head throughout the lift.

4. Once casualties are landed, they can be moved to a safe position for resuscitation, first aid or aftercare.

THE ASSISTED LIFT

This is used to land casualties from deep water and must be performed by two or more lifeguards (Fig. 5-44). This skill should be practised by all team members, including support staff in pools with only one lifeguard on duty. It can be very difficult for a lone lifeguard to remove a casualty from deep water.

Assuming other team members are ready on the pool side, one of them should take charge. This can be the rescuing lifeguard, who may be too tired by the rescue to help with the lift itself.

Who does what will depend on the number of team members available and the provisions of the pool's EAP. Helpers in the water can assist by lifting and supporting the casualty's hips. If lifeguards are confident that pool users or other swimmers can safely assist under instruction, they should be asked to do so. To perform an assisted lift, follow the procedure in the panel (left).

Landing casualties who have a suspected spinal cord injury is a specialist skill and is covered in Chapter Eight.

MULTIPLE RESCUES

A pool user who gets into difficulty may panic and grab the nearest person in the pool or someone may go to help, only to find they get into difficulty themselves. So lifeguards sometimes have to rescue two or, less frequently, three or more casualties who are clutching one another. This situation may arise during both recreational and programmed swimming sessions.

Multiple rescues often need the support of the whole lifeguard team and it may be necessary for more than one lifeguard to enter the water. In a multiple rescue, the use of a buoyant device such as a torpedo buoy is almost essential and is very strongly recommended

It may not always be necessary to separate the casualties when rescuing them. They can often be towed together to a point of support. Once there, feeling more secure, they can more easily be persuaded to separate. If the pool has a shallow end, it is better to tow the casualties there so they can stand on the pool bottom.

Towing two separated casualties is a difficult task for a single lifeguard. It can be distressing for the casualties as well. One of the most practical methods is the double arm tow but this can result in constant splashing of water into the casualties' faces. Even with a double arm tow, the casualties' faces may not be sufficiently clear of the water to prevent them becoming distressed. So a double contact tow is not recommended unless absolutely essential (Fig. 5-47). If two casualties are towed together to a deep water point of support, it is essential that the weaker swimmer is supported first and the other immediately after.

Sometimes, one or other of the casualties may be unconscious. Lifeguards should use the various rescue methods described in this chapter, including techniques of turning casualties and tows using buoyant devices.

BUOYANT AID MULTIPLE RESCUES

The lifeguard should swim to the casualties with a torpedo buoy as described earlier in this chapter. The buoy should be placed in front of the two casualties and one or both of them instructed to take hold of it. The casualties should then be towed to a point of support from where the lifeguard team can help them out of the water (Figs. 5-45 and 5-46).

Both casualties should be brought to the point of support at the same time. The weaker swimmer can be instructed to hold on first while the second casualty keeps hold of the torpedo buoy.

SEPARATING CASUALTIES

Sometimes it is necessary to separate two casualties who are clinging to one another in the water. The procedure is:

- grasp the uppermost casualty under the armpits from behind;
- force both casualties under the water;
- place both legs around the first casualty and the feet against the hips and thighs of the second casualty;
- maintain a grip on the first casualty's body; then
- straighten the legs to force the two casualties apart.

If possible, give a torpedo buoy to the stronger casualty for support then tow the other casualty to safety using the most

FIGURE 5-45
RESCUING TWO CASUALTIES USING A TORPEDO BUOY.

FIGURE 5-46
ONE CASUALTY HOLDS ONTO THE TORPEDO BUOY.

FIGURE 5-47
DOUBLE CONTACT TOW.

FIGURE 5-48
A LIFEGUARD TRAINING
SESSION.

appropriate method. Alternatively, tow both casualties to a point of support, preferably in shallow water (Fig. 5-47). Be prepared to release the tow if either casualty struggles further or the rescue is failing. Summon support from other members of the lifeguard team to complete the rescue.

BRINGING RESCUE SKILLS TOGETHER

This chapter has described a wide variety of rescue skills, including:

- reaching and throwing;
- entering the pool safely;
- wading, swimming and towing;
- using buoyant aids;
- rescues from under water; and
- recovering unconscious casualties.

These skills will be taught separately during Foundation Module training and will be used according to the EAP of the pool where lifeguards are working.

Any one of these skills may enable a lifeguard to effect a rescue but usually a combination of them will be required. Sometimes a particularly difficult, awkward, or totally unpredictable incident will occur for which there is no prescribed method and techniques will need to be mixed and adapted as necessary. But the skills described above should cover most situations lifeguards are likely to encounter.

It is vital that these skills are rehearsed and practised regularly, especially in the context of the sort of emergencies that are likely to occur in the particular pool where the lifeguard works. Continued training is the essence of good practice and lifeguards should constantly strive to improve and develop their knowledge and skills (Fig. 5-48).

TEST YOURSELF

1. Describe some of the significant features of a typical rescue.

2. What are the advantages of a fixed focal point for rescues?

3. In what circumstances might a shout-and-signal rescue be appropriate?

4. What are the dangers associated with old-fashioned lifebuoys?

5. What sort of equipment might be used in a reaching rescue?

6. Name the most common item of equipment used for throwing resubmerged casualties.

7. What precautions should be taken during a throwing rescue?

8. What effects might buoyancy have during a wading rescue?

9. Describe three ways of entering the water to perform a rescue.

10. Name two swimming strokes recommended for rescues.

11. What is meant by treading water?

12. Describe the eggbeater kick.

13. Name three ways of reaching the bottom of the pool.

14. Describe how to release pressure on the ears from swimming under water.

15. Why do lifeguards need training in releases and escapes?

16. Describe how to escape from a front grasp.

17. Describe how to turn an unconscious casualty in the water.

18. Which tows can be used in standing depth water?

19. What type of injury is most likely to result from poor lifting technique?

20. Describe some techniques to make lifting safer.

21. When would a stirrup lift be used?

22. Describe an assisted lift.

23. How would you separate two casualties in the water?

6

Resuscitation

Resuscitation

ESUSCITATION is the act of attempting to revive a nearly dead or apparently dead casualty. The aim of resuscitation is to preserve life until qualified and equipped medical assistance can be obtained.

As lifeguards are often the first people to attend a casualty at a swimming pool, they may have to undertake resuscitation or give other medical assistance.

Casualty recognition and diagnosis are skills all lifeguards need. Swift action is essential because the longer the casualty is left, the more difficult recovery becomes.

Before resuscitation, lifeguards may have to rescue casualties and bring them to a position of safety. They must also be able to assume responsibility for managing casualties' medical conditions. So Foundation Module training includes basic anatomy and physiology (the structure and function of the human body), cardio pulmonary resuscitation (CPR), and first aid.

Lifeguards must keep their resuscitation and first aid skills up to date. They must be trained to use the equipment at the pool where they work (Fig. 6-1). This equipment might include:

- resuscitation kits (oxygen insufflation);
- first aid kits;
- spine boards;
- stretchers and other equipment for transporting casualties; and
- training manikins.

RLSS UK advocates the use of resuscitation manikins for training and assessment (Fig. 6-2). A list of approved manikins is available from RLSS UK at Mountbatten House. The address appears at the front of this book.

FIGURE 6-1
FIRST AID EQUIPMENT.

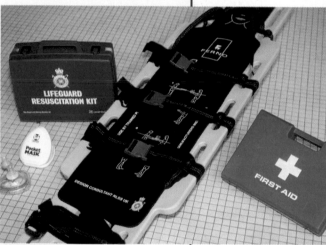

FIGURE 6-2
RESUSCITATION MANIKINS.

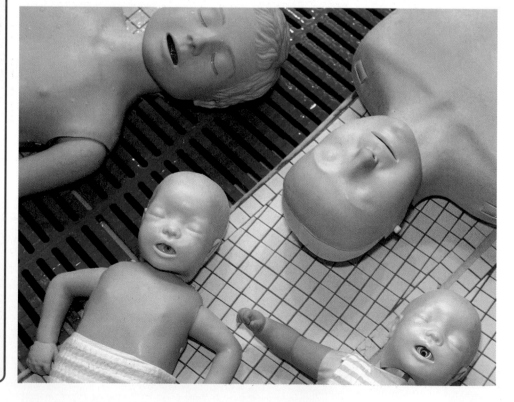

BASIC ANATOMY AND PHYSIOLOGY

Lifeguards should have a general understanding of basic anatomy and the body's systems. This knowledge will help them deal with emergencies and promote the recovery of casualties.

Understanding respiration and blood circulation will help lifeguards to undertake cardio pulmonary resuscitation (CPR) more effectively. The word 'cardio' is the medical term for matters relating to the heart and the word 'pulmonary' for matters relating to the lungs. However, respiration and circulation are only two of the many systems that must operate as part of a whole if the body is to function normally (Fig. 6-3).

The body is built up on a skeleton of bones. The skeleton gives the body shape and support and helps protect the internal organs. To allow movement, muscles are connected to the bones either side of a joint. When these muscles shorten (contract) movement occurs. The muscles are controlled by nerve impulses passing from the brain and through the spinal cord (Fig. 6-4, page 106). The spinal cord lies protected within the spine. The nerves themselves travel outwards from the spinal cord so that impulses from the brain can be translated into purposeful movement. As well as voluntary movement (such as walking), the body relies on involuntary movement (such as the beating of the heart) to survive.

Movement depends on energy. The energy to contract muscles comes from the food we eat. Food is digested and broken down in the stomach and small intestine and absorbed into the blood. The liver stores the digested food in a form that can be used to produce energy and has an important role in making harmful substances safe. Unwanted food and other waste products are passed out either through the intestines or in a fluid form through the kidneys.

Oxygen is vital for energy production and comes from the air which is breathed in. The air is taken into the lungs which diffuse the oxygen into the blood. This process is called respiration.

The heart pumps the oxygenated blood through the arteries to all parts of the body. When the oxygen has been used, the blood returns through the veins to the lungs where it is recharged with oxygen. This process is called circulation and the functions of the body rely on this oxygen carried in the blood. Without oxygen, the body will cease to function (Fig. 6-3).

Some organs are more vulnerable to lack of oxygen than others. The brain is the most sensitive part of the body and the most vulnerable to lack of oxygen. If the heart stops, the blood stops circulating and therefore no oxygen is carried to the brain. So within seconds of the heart stopping, the victim loses consciousness from the lack of oxygen and after a few minutes dies. Therefore it is absolutely vital to start cardio pulmonary resuscitation as soon as possible after breathing and the heart have stopped, whatever the cause.

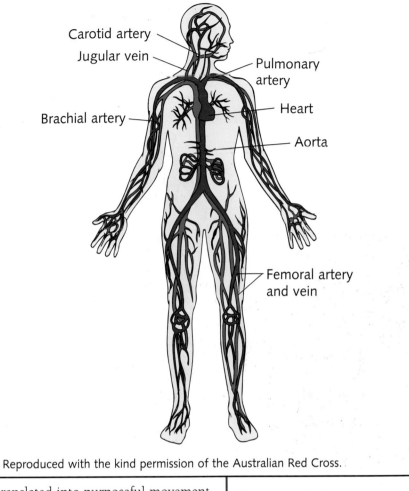

Carotid artery
Jugular vein
Pulmonary artery
Brachial artery
Heart
Aorta
Femoral artery and vein

Reproduced with the kind permission of the Australian Red Cross.

FIGURE 6-3
BODY CIRCULATION.

FIGURE 6-4 ANATOMY OF SPINE AND SPINAL CORD.

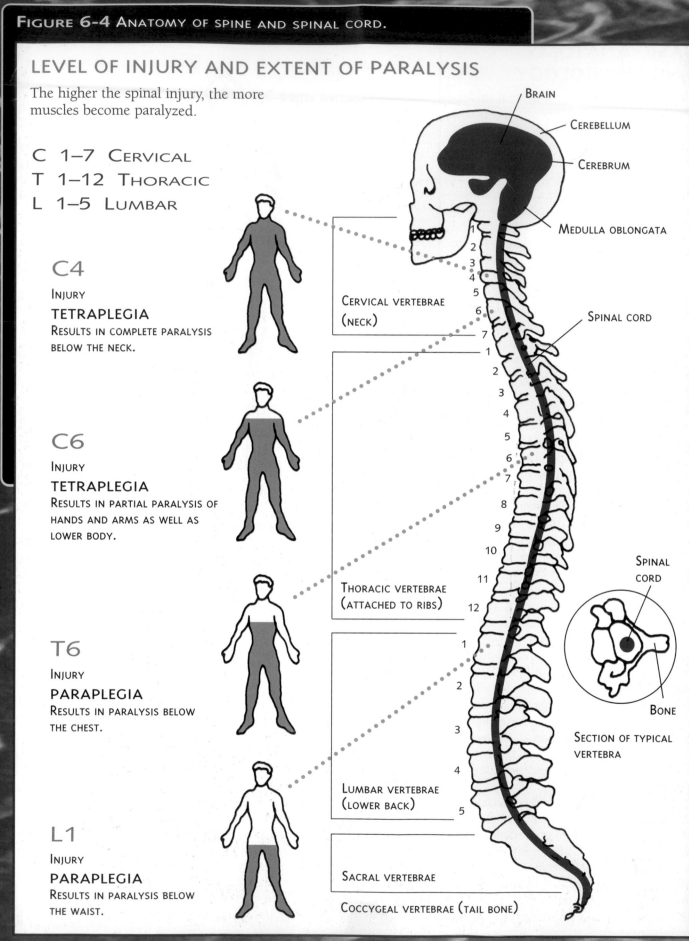

LEVEL OF INJURY AND EXTENT OF PARALYSIS

The higher the spinal injury, the more muscles become paralyzed.

C 1–7 CERVICAL
T 1–12 THORACIC
L 1–5 LUMBAR

C4
INJURY
TETRAPLEGIA
RESULTS IN COMPLETE PARALYSIS BELOW THE NECK.

C6
INJURY
TETRAPLEGIA
RESULTS IN PARTIAL PARALYSIS OF HANDS AND ARMS AS WELL AS LOWER BODY.

T6
INJURY
PARAPLEGIA
RESULTS IN PARALYSIS BELOW THE CHEST.

L1
INJURY
PARAPLEGIA
RESULTS IN PARALYSIS BELOW THE WAIST.

BRAIN
CEREBELLUM
CEREBRUM
MEDULLA OBLONGATA

CERVICAL VERTEBRAE (NECK)

SPINAL CORD

THORACIC VERTEBRAE (ATTACHED TO RIBS)

SPINAL CORD

BONE

SECTION OF TYPICAL VERTEBRA

LUMBAR VERTEBRAE (LOWER BACK)

SACRAL VERTEBRAE

COCCYGEAL VERTEBRAE (TAIL BONE)

Reproduced with the kind permission of the Spinal Injuries Association.

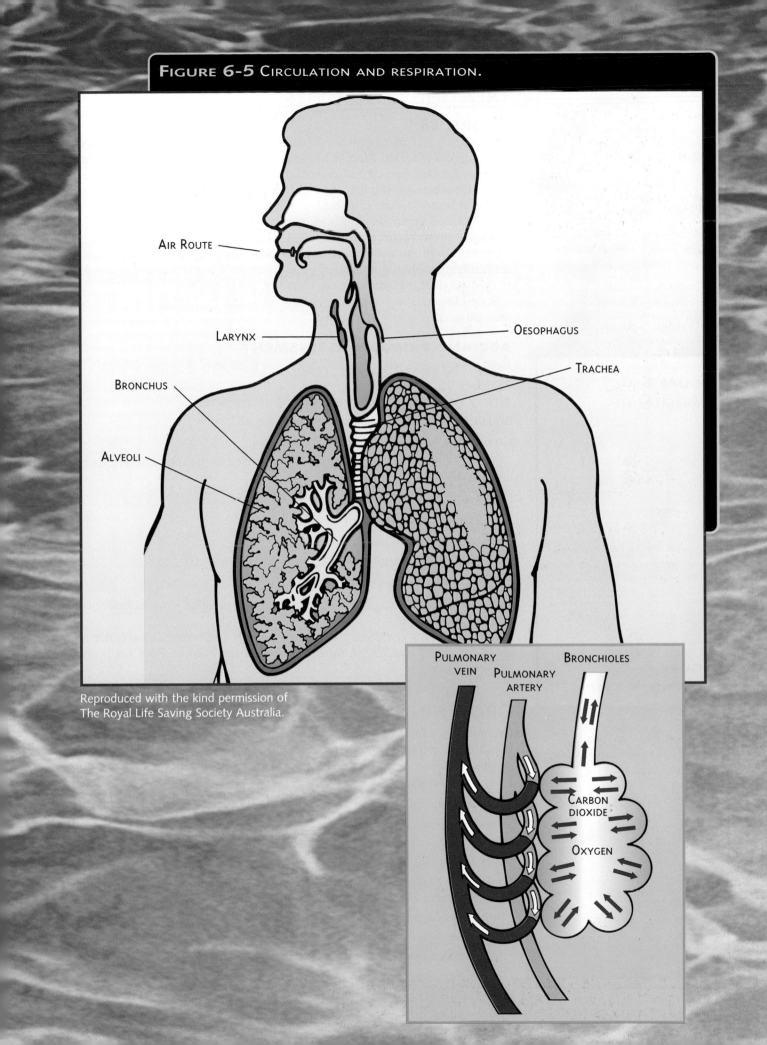

FIGURE 6-5 CIRCULATION AND RESPIRATION.

AIR ROUTE

LARYNX

OESOPHAGUS

TRACHEA

BRONCHUS

ALVEOLI

Reproduced with the kind permission of
The Royal Life Saving Society Australia.

PULMONARY VEIN

PULMONARY ARTERY

BRONCHIOLES

CARBON DIOXIDE

OXYGEN

FIGURE 6-6
RESUSCITATION.

TREATING CASUALTIES

PRIORITIES

The way in which an emergency is handled at a particular pool will be governed by its Emergency Action Plan (EAP) and this will be covered in training for the Professional (Site Specific) Module of the NPLQ. However, there are universal priorities for administering first aid and resuscitation. Training in these is covered by the Foundation Module (Fig. 6-6).

In a medical emergency on land or in the water, lifeguards must prioritise their actions to preserve life, minimise injury and promote recovery.

Control of the situation and the safety of all involved is the first essential. Other team members should be alerted or summoned. Lifeguards should check for any immediate danger threatening the casualties or themselves.

Once casualties are out of danger (for instance, by having been rescued), their medical condition can be assessed.

ABC AND PRIMARY ASSESSMENT

Note the casualty's responses and determine their level of consciousness. Check the ABC of:

Airway — ensure the airway is open and unobstructed;

Breathing — look, listen, feel for breathing; and

Circulation — check the pulse for circulation.

Life threatening conditions must be attended to before less serious ones are tackled. Prioritise treatment as follows:

1 Cardio pulmonary resuscitation.

2 Control of severe bleeding.

3 Management of choking.

4 Care of unconscious, breathing casualties.

5 Treatment for shock.

In some cases bleeding may be so severe that it must be stopped before resuscitation can be effective.

If the casualty is conscious, breathing normally and resuscitation is not required, check for severe bleeding or other life threatening injuries. First aid is covered in Chapter Seven.

FIGURE 6-7
A DROWNING CASUALTY.

DROWNING

Drowning is a form of asphyxia. Asphyxia describes the medical condition where insufficient oxygen reaches the blood because breathing is impaired or has stopped. Asphyxia can be due to many causes apart from drowning. Among the most common are:

• fluid in the lungs stopping oxygen being transferred to the blood;

• suffocation (described below);

• failure of the blood to carry oxygen from causes such as gas poisoning or severe bleeding; or

• breathing failure due to chest injury, deep unconsciousness, drug overdose, electric shock and so on.

Suffocation describes conditions where air is unable to reach the lungs. There can be many causes. Among the most common are:

• the tongue blocking the throat of an unconscious casualty;

• a foreign object stuck in the throat;

- strangulation, and
- the mouth and nose getting accidentally covered, for instance by a plastic bag.

Drowning may be described as death from asphyxia caused by immersion in water. Near drowning describes a situation where the casualty survives but would have drowned had they not been recovered from the water and revived.

Drowning incidents in swimming pools vary widely, depending on the individual involved and the particular circumstances. In some cases, casualties slip below the water unnoticed (Fig. 6-7). These 'silent drownings' often result from activities not directly related to swimming. In other drownings, casualties panic and make noticeable (and possibly violent) attempts to keep their heads above water. Panic invariably adds to a casualty's difficulties.

Whatever the type of incident, there are certain features common to all drownings.

In the initial stages of drowning, when the casualty's head goes under, water entering the mouth usually results in the closure of the airway. This action is similar to that which prevents food and liquid entering the lungs during swallowing. A drowning casualty's airway remains sealed as a safety mechanism to prevent water entering the lungs. This creates a situation where there can be no breathing and is called apnoea.

Lifeguard intervention at this stage (such as lifting the casualty's head clear of the water and ensuring an open airway) should ensure breathing restarts (Fig. 6-8). However, if no assistance is given the casualty will swallow more water and sink lower.

During the initial stages of apnoea the limited oxygen available will be diverted to the brain and other vital organs. The gradual reduction in oxygen to the brain (called hypoxia) can lead to confusion so lifeguards should not expect near drowning casualties to always respond in a normal manner.

In the later stages of drowning the casualty will become unconscious and stop breathing altogether. This state is known as terminal apnoea. The casualty will require resuscitation to restart breathing, usually by means of rescue breathing (also called expired air ventilation and described in detail later in this chapter). After successful resuscitation, they will need urgent medical attention.

If the casualty becomes unconscious in the water, the reflex spasm which closed the airway may relax, allowing it to reopen. As this happens, water will enter the lungs. If any air enters with the water it may be utilised, but the casualty will continue to breathe in more and more water as they sink. This is usually called 'wet drowning'.

The presence of water in the lungs may damage the air sacs. This will dramatically reduce the efficiency of the lungs, so even when the casualty is rescued they will require urgent medical attention.

A complication can result from water which is swallowed rather than breathed. Swallowing large amounts of water often leads to vomiting. The casualty may then breathe the vomit into the airway and lungs. Another problem is that substances called surfactants can be washed from the surfaces of the lungs and can cause frothing at the mouth.

In a minority of drownings (mostly those involving children), the airway will remain closed and no water will enter the lungs. This condition is usually called 'dry drowning'.

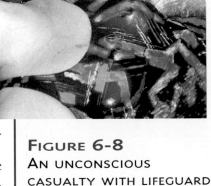

FIGURE 6-8
AN UNCONSCIOUS CASUALTY WITH LIFEGUARD SUPPORTING HEAD.

HYPERVENTILATION

Hyperventilation (rapid, deep breathing) may have caused many otherwise unexplained drownings and near drownings. It results from rapid, repeated deep breaths. Some swimmers think this will increase the oxygen content of their blood and thus prolong the time they can spend underwater.

But hyperventilation doesn't increase the oxygen content in the blood. It does, however, reduce the blood's level of carbon dioxide. The carbon dioxide level helps the brain control breathing. As the level falls, the desire to breathe is reduced. Physical activity will then use up the oxygen in the blood before the carbon dioxide level has reached the point where it restores normal breathing. The swimmer effectively runs out of oxygen and loses consciousness.

AFTER EFFECTS OF NEAR DROWNING

Secondary drowning is a danger which is often associated with near drownings. Even a small amount of water in the lungs will interfere with the normal transfer of oxygen to the blood. The water also irritates the air sacs in the lungs causing them to produce a fluid which further impairs oxygen transfer.

The effects of secondary drowning can be delayed for up to 72 hours, so it is important to maintain observation of any casualty who has been submerged or involved in a near drowning even if they appear to have made a full recovery.

A condition called post immersion collapse may follow submersion if it has lasted for hours rather than minutes. The squeezing effect of the water pressure can cause loss of fluid, including blood plasma, through the kidneys. Once revived, the casualty's body can be left with insufficient blood and fluid so circulation is inadequate and signs of shock may appear.

Follow up medical attention is essential in all near drownings or incidents where casualties have been submerged.

CARDIAC ARREST

The term cardiac arrest means the heart is no longer pumping blood around the body. The heart may have stopped beating altogether (asystole) or be twitching in a completely irregular and ineffective way (ventricular fibrillation). In both cases, the circulation will have stopped and there will be no pulse.

The techniques of resuscitation are the same for both forms of cardiac arrest. The difference between them cannot be diagnosed without an electrocardiogram and only becomes important when specialist medical assistance arrives.

Cardiac arrest may be due to the lack of oxygen resulting from asphyxia (which, as we have seen, includes drowning). Other causes include direct damage to the heart, coronary thrombosis (a heart attack), or electric shock.

Whatever the cause of cardiac arrest, the result is profound. Within seconds of the heart stopping, the casualty will lose consciousness and, if the heart is not restarted, will die within a few minutes. That is why resuscitation must be started as soon as possible.

Resuscitation buys time until qualified professional medical assistance arrives. Medical aid must be summoned at the earliest opportunity. For instance, as soon as an unconscious casualty has been identified, one team member should telephone for an ambulance while others perform a rescue and start resuscitation.

The key stages can be expressed as a chain of survival.

- The first stage is to promote early access to the casualty by medical professionals.

- The second stage is immediate cardio pulmonary resuscitation to buy time.

- The third stage is electrical defibrillation of the heart to restart it.

- The fourth stage is specialised advanced life support to stabilise the casualty.

THE RESUSCITATION SEQUENCE

Resuscitation is needed if the heart has stopped beating or if breathing is inadequate or has stopped.

Resuscitation will not always revive casualties. It is a means of buying time until more specialised medical aid (such as electrical defibrillation) arrives. It is therefore vital to summon medical assistance immediately.

Pool lifeguards work as part of a team so even in a small pool they should be able to call on trained support in an emergency. Even if there is no other lifeguard to assist in CPR, other pool staff such as receptionists, cleaners or security officers can assist. However limited the back up, someone **must** summon medical assistance, usually by telephoning for an ambulance, and this function will usually be set out in the EAP.

Lifeguards will receive specific training in dealing with emergency situations at the pool where they work during their Professional (Site Specific) Module training. However, certain general principles apply to resuscitating casualties in any situation.

The sequence below assumes the lifeguard(s) and casualty(ies) are in a safe position (usually out of the pool if there has been an in-water emergency).

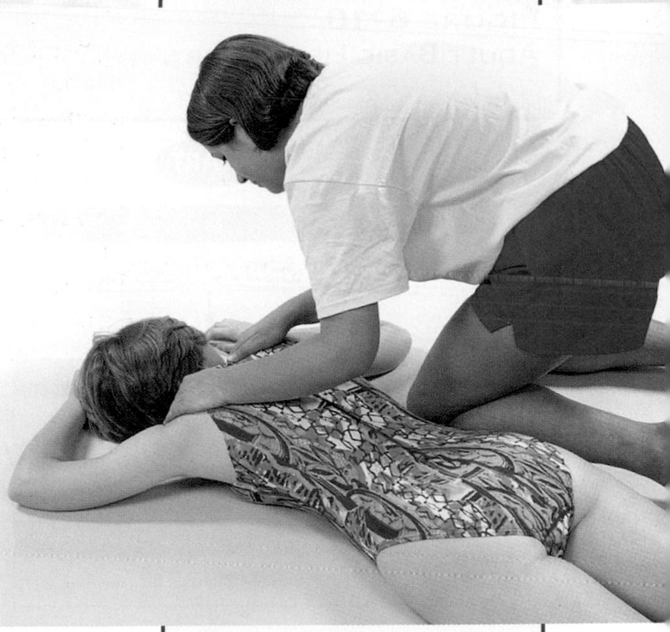

FIGURE 6-9
CHECK RESPONSE.

CHECK RESPONSIVENESS:

Check whether the casualty is responsive, semi-conscious or unconscious (Fig. 6-9). This can be done in the water during a rescue and repeated once the casualty is on the pool side. If the casualty is responsive, check for any injuries and provide the appropriate treatment and support as detailed elsewhere in this book.

IF THE CASUALTY IS UNCONSCIOUS:

- alert support staff and other team members;
- ensure someone telephones for an ambulance or summons qualified medical aid; and
- open the casualty's airway and check for breathing.

IF THE CASUALTY IS BREATHING:

If no injury to the spine or neck is suspected and no sign of other major injury:

- turn the casualty into the recovery position; and
- summon further medical aid as appropriate.

IF THE CASUALTY IS NOT BREATHING:

- give two effective rescue breaths;
- ensure other team members are in support; then
- check for signs of a circulation.

IF THERE ARE NO SIGNS OF A CIRCULATION:

- start chest compression;
- combine chest compression and rescue breathing (CPR); and
- summon urgent medical assistance as set out in the EAP.

CONTINUE RESUSCITATION UNTIL:

- the casualty shows signs of life;
- qualified medical help arrives; or
- you are too exhausted to continue.

FIGURE 6-10
ADULT BASIC LIFE SUPPORT.

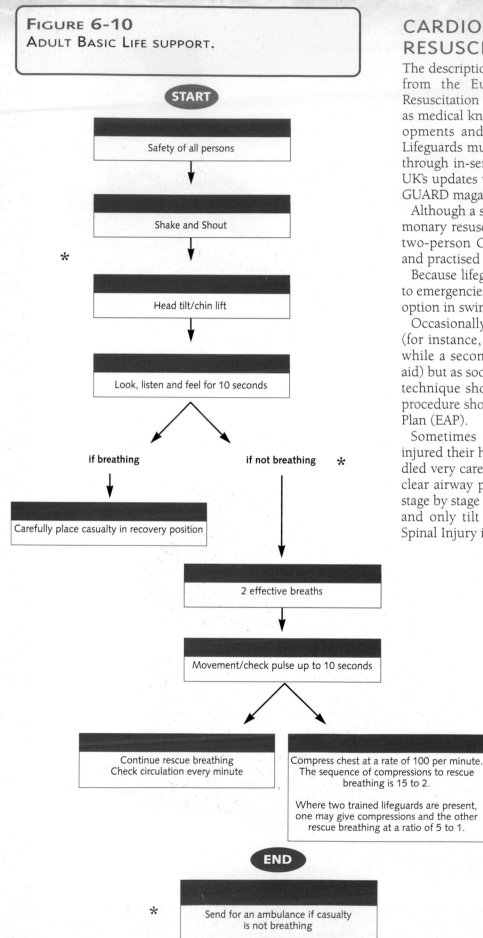

START

Safety of all persons

Shake and Shout

*

Head tilt/chin lift

Look, listen and feel for 10 seconds

if breathing   if not breathing   *

Carefully place casualty in recovery position

2 effective breaths

Movement/check pulse up to 10 seconds

Continue rescue breathing
Check circulation every minute

Compress chest at a rate of 100 per minute.
The sequence of compressions to rescue
breathing is 15 to 2.

Where two trained lifeguards are present,
one may give compressions and the other
rescue breathing at a ratio of 5 to 1.

END

*   Send for an ambulance if casualty
is not breathing

CARDIO PULMONARY RESUSCITATION

The description of CPR below accords with guidance from the European Resuscitation Council, the Resuscitation Council (UK) and RLSS UK. However, as medical knowledge advances, there may be developments and changes in the techniques of CPR. Lifeguards must keep their practice up to date, both through in-service training and by referring to RLSS UK's updates which are published regularly in LIFEGUARD magazine and through RLSS UK Branches.

Although a single person can undertake cardio pulmonary resuscitation, RLSS UK always recommends two-person CPR when lifeguards are fully trained and practised in the technique. (Fig 6-10)

Because lifeguards are part of a team in responding to emergencies, two-person CPR is usually a practical option in swimming pool incidents.

Occasionally, one lifeguard may have to start CPR (for instance, before other team members arrive or while a second lifeguard goes to summon medical aid) but as soon as two trained people are present the technique should change to two-person CPR. The procedure should be set out in the Emergency Action Plan (EAP).

Sometimes casualties requiring CPR may have injured their head, neck or spine. They must be handled very carefully. When lifting the chin to ensure a clear airway prior to rescue breathing, tilt the head stage by stage ensuring as little movement as possible and only tilt just far enough to open the airway. Spinal Injury is dealt with in Chapter Eight.

CHECKING AIRWAY AND BREATHING

Checking the airway

The first priority is to ensure an open airway. Loosen any constrictions around the casualty's neck and remove any obvious obstruction from the mouth. Remove loose dentures but leave tight, well fitting ones in place.

Turn the casualty onto their back if not already in this position. Place one hand along the casualty's forehead and press back gently to tilt the head. Keep the thumb and index finger of the same hand free because if rescue breathing is required they will gently squeeze the nose to close the nostrils.

With the other hand, place the fingertips under the point of the chin. Lift the chin gently. Sometimes this will allow breathing to restart (Fig. 6-11).

Checking breathing

Check for breathing. Look for chest movements. Listen at the mouth for breathing sounds while looking at the chest. With your cheek close to the casualty's mouth, feel for any movement of air for ten sconds (Fig. 6-12).

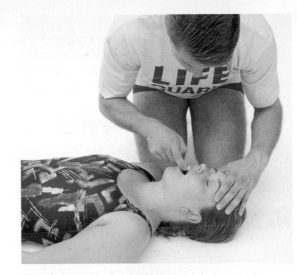

FIGURE 6-11
CHECK THE AIRWAY.

FIGURE 6-12
CHECK FOR MOVEMENT OF AIR.

RESCUE BREATHING (EXPIRED AIR VENTILATION)

Rescue breathing is often called expired air ventilation and is also sometimes referred to as 'the kiss of life'. It is the most effective technique of artificial respiration that doesn't rely on special equipment. Basically, it consists of blowing air into the casualty's lungs by putting the mouth over the casualty's mouth or nose. Although the exhaled air contains only 17% oxygen (compared with 21% in the atmosphere), this is quite enough to keep the casualty alive.

If the casualty is still breathing weakly, rescue breathing will do no harm. In fact, if the casualty's breathing is weak rescue breathing will be beneficial.

Rescue breathing can be given by trained people of any age but some people may be deterred because they consider it an unpleasant procedure. Lifeguards, however, have a duty to respond appropriately to emergency situations and distaste can never be allowed to compromise this responsibility.

Drowning and near drowning victims often vomit, as described under the heading 'PROBLEMS WITH RESUSCITATION'. This may mean using the mouth-to-nose technique rather than mouth-to-mouth. The two methods are equally effective in ensuring ventilation.

Concern about HIV (the AIDS virus) may also arise. Although the virus has been found in saliva, no known cases of HIV infection have resulted from mouth-to-mouth or mouth-to-nose rescue breathing so lifeguards should not be deterred from using the technique in an emergency. However, it is recommended that ventilation masks, which provide a barrier to direct contact, are used because they offer protection against other infections and give peace of mind (Fig. 6-13).

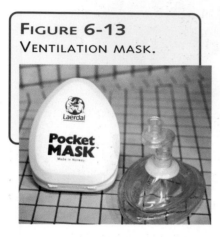

FIGURE 6-13
VENTILATION MASK.

HOW TO GIVE RESCUE BREATHING

If the casualty is not breathing but has signs of a circulation, rescue breathing should be started.

- With the casualty on their back, maintain the head tilt and chin lift described above (Fig. 6-14 A).
- Using the index finger and thumb, pinch the soft part of the casualty's nose to ensure the nostrils are closed.
- Allow the casualty's mouth to open a little while still maintaining the head tilt and chin lift.
- Take a full breath and place the lips around the casualty's mouth, making sure there is a good airtight seal.
- Breath steadily into the casualty's mouth until you see their chest rise, taking about $1\frac{1}{2}-2$ seconds for the full inflation.
- Remove your mouth from the casualty's mouth and allow their chest to sink fully as the air comes out while still maintaining the head tilt and chin lift (Fig. 6-14B).
- Take another full breath and repeat the sequence above ten times.
- Ten full inflations of the casualty's chest should take about one minute and the breaths should follow one another rhythmically.

Ten rescue breath inflations should be well within the capability of a normally fit lifeguard. About once every minute, check for signs of circulation by feeling the carotid (neck) pulse and looking for any movement as described below (Fig. 6-14 C).

If signs of a circulation (such as the pulse) are present but the casualty has not resumed breathing, continue rescue breathing, checking the signs of circulation about once a minute. Be ready to change to full cardio pulmonary resuscitation if the pulse disappears. With the support of other team members, continue rescue breathing until medical aid arrives.

If the casualty resumes breathing but their breath is very weak or shallow, rescue breathing should be continued. Inflations should be at the same time and rate as the casualty's own respiration in order to supplement it.

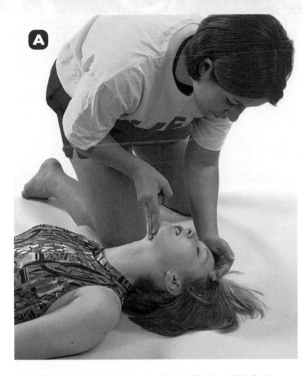

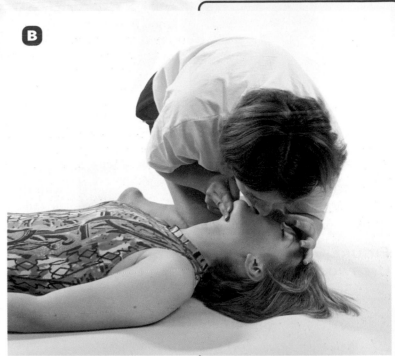

CHECKING FOR A CIRCULATION

Check for signs of circulation by feeling for a pulse and looking for any movement by the casualty. The best place to feel for the pulse is the neck. The pulse which can be found either side of the Adam's apple is called the carotid pulse.

To feel for the carotid pulse, keep the casualty's head tilted. If working from the side of the casualty, slide two fingers sideways from the Adam's apple until you feel a strap-like muscle. The carotid pulse can be felt just beneath this muscle (Fig. 6-14C).

Feel for the pulse for no more than ten seconds before deciding whether it is absent.

CHEST COMPRESSION

Chest compression maintains the circulation of the blood when the heart has stopped and can sometimes start it beating again. The technique consists of rhythmical compressions of the casualty's chest, achieved by pressing down with the hands onto the casualty's breastbone.

There is some risk of damage to the heart, chest wall and abdominal organs during chest compression. This risk is far outweighed by lifesaving potential but it does mean that it is important to be confident of the diagnosis of cardiac arrest before starting.

Even the most skilful cardio pulmonary resuscitation may not always result in a casualty's recovery. The heart may have been damaged or there may have been too long a delay before resuscitation started. Inevitably, casualties sometimes die. If lifeguards have undertaken resuscitation correctly and carefully, they have no cause for self criticism or guilt. Of course, a death is always upsetting and, as we have seen, can lead to post traumatic stress disorder. Lifeguards should be aware of this and be prepared to seek counselling if necessary.

FIGURE 6-14
A TILT HEAD BACK.
B WATCH FOR CHEST MOVEMENT.
C FEEL FOR PULSE.

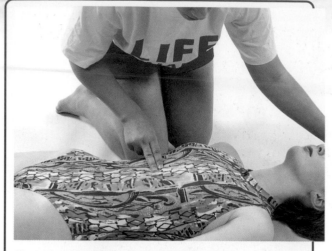

FIGURE 6-15
USE TWO FINGERS...

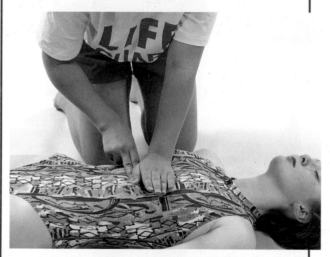

FIGURE 6-16
...TO FIND THE CORRECT POSITION.

FIGURE 6-17
KEEP YOUR ARMS STRAIGHT.

HOW TO GIVE SINGLE-PERSON CPR

If there are no signs of a circulation, make sure emergency medical aid has been summoned and start cardio pulmonary resuscitation, combining rescue breathing and chest compression.

The technique for two-person CPR is described after that for a single person. Remember that CPR should be undertaken by two trained people whenever possible except in the case of babies and children under about eight years of age (see later in this chapter).

The casualty should be on her back on a firm, flat surface with the head tilted and chin lifted to open the airway as described above.

- Give two inflations of rescue breathing, taking about $1\frac{1}{2}$–2 seconds for each. The second breath should start as soon as the casualty's chest has fallen after the first one.

- Using the index and middle fingers, locate the bottom of the casualty's ribs. Keeping the fingers together, slide them upwards to the point where the ribs join the bottom of the casualty's breastbone (Fig. 6-15).

- Put the middle finger on this spot, then place the index finger on the casualty's breastbone above the spot.

- Slide the heel of the other hand down the breastbone until it reaches the index finger. This spot should be the middle of the lower half of the breastbone (Fig 6-16).

- Place the heel of the first hand on top of the other one then interlock the fingers of both hands to ensure the pressure is not applied over the ribs.

- Lean well over the casualty with the arms straight and press down vertically on the breastbone to depress it about four or five centimetres (about $1\frac{3}{4}$–2 inches). Apply no more pressure than necessary to achieve this (Fig. 6-17).

- Release the pressure but don't lift the hands away from the casualty's chest.

- Repeat at the rate of about 100 compressions a minute. This rate equals just under two compressions each second and it may help to count out loud "one and two and three..." and so on.

- After fifteen compressions (which will take about ten seconds), tilt the casualty's head, lift the chin and give two inflations of rescue breathing.

- After the two inflations, immediately return the hands to the breastbone and give a further fifteen compressions.

Continue the sequence of compressions and inflations until other team members can assist, the medical services arrive or until exhausted.

> **Remember, the single person ratio is 15 compressions to 2 breaths.**

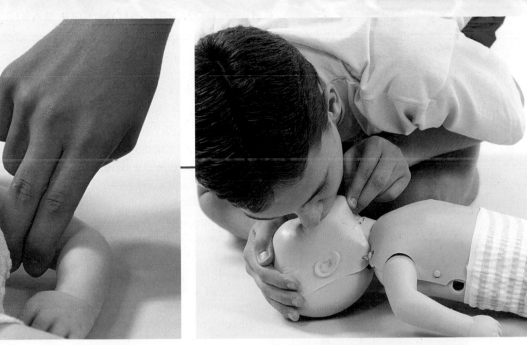

FIGURE 6-18
THE BRACHIAL (ARM) PULSE.

FIGURE 6-19
COVER A BABY'S NOSE *AND* MOUTH.

CPR FOR BABIES AND CHILDREN

Two-person resuscitation is not appropriate for babies or younger children

For the purposes of resuscitation, a 'baby' is defined as a child in the first year of life. A 'younger child' is considered to be up to the age of about eight years. An 'older child' is from about eight years old to adulthood.

When carrying out resuscitation of babies or children, the techniques of rescue breathing and chest compression are similar to those for an adult, modified to allow for the difference in size and the immaturity of the casualty.

Because a baby's neck is short and fat, it is difficult to feel the carotid (neck) pulse. Instead, check the brachial (arm) pulse, which is felt along the inside of the upper arm (Fig. 6-18).

It is rare for a baby's or a child's heart to stop unexpectedly (cardiac arrest). Problems with breathing are far more common and, if not treated rapidly and correctly, may lead to cardiac arrest due to lack of oxygen in the blood. Particular attention must be given to obtaining a clear airway in any baby or child whose heart has stopped or who has stopped breathing. This may include action to relieve choking.

In babies and children breathing may become obstructed or stop because of:

- submersion in water (near drowning);
- inhalation of vomit, regurgitated food, or a foreign body;
- injuries to the head, neck, or chest; or
- infection of the throat (croup) or lungs (pneumonia).

RESCUE BREATHING FOR BABIES AND CHILDREN

As with adults, rescue breathing should aim to cause the chest to rise as in normal breathing. Each breath should take about $1-1\frac{1}{2}$ seconds. For babies, the lifeguard's mouth should be placed over the baby's mouth and nose (Fig. 6-19) and give 5 breaths of rescue breathing. For a child, the normal mouth-to-mouth position can be used.

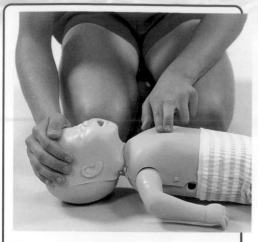

FIGURE 6-20
FINDING THE CORRECT POSITION.

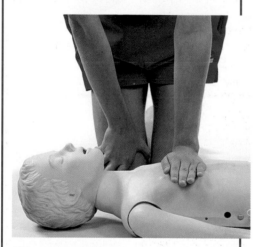

FIGURE 6-21
USE ONE HAND FOR YOUNGER
CHILDREN.

FIGURE 6-22
TWO-PERSON CPR.

CHEST COMPRESSION FOR BABIES AND CHILDREN

- Lay the casualty on the back on a firm surface.
- For a baby, find the correct position on the chest by imagining a line joining the nipples and placing two fingers on the breastbone just below the mid point of this line (Fig. 6-20).
- For a younger child, find the correct position on the chest as you would for an adult.
- Use only two fingers for the compressions for a baby and one hand for the compressions for younger children (Fig 6-21).
- For babies and younger children, compress about one third of the depth of the chest.
- For babies and younger children, chest compression and rescue breathing should at the ratio of five compressions to one breath (**5 to 1**). **At a rate of 100 compressions per minute.**
- For older children, increase the depth of compression up to the adult figure of 4-5 cms. As the adult depth of compression is reached, two hands will be needed on the chest. At this point change to a ratio of fifteen compressions to two breaths (**15 to 2**).

HOW TO GIVE TWO-PERSON CPR

With two trained people undertaking CPR, one can give rescue breathing while the other gives chest compression at a ratio of five compressions to each breath (Fig. 6-22). This results in better ventilation of the casualty and less interruption in chest compression. However, two-person CPR should **not** be attempted if the casualty is a younger child or baby.

> **Remember, the two-person ratio is 5 compressions to 1 breath.**

Two-person CPR is the preferred method when both people are trained and competent in the technique. If, however, they have only been taught the single person method, they should take turns to administer CPR at the ratio of fifteen compressions to two breaths.

The casualty should on their back on a firm, flat surface with the head tilted and chin lifted to open the airway as described above.

In some cases, a lifeguard will have started cardio pulmonary resuscitation before another team member arrives to assist. When changing from one to two-person CPR, the incoming person usually takes over chest compression after the original person has given two rescue breaths. During these two breaths, the incoming person should locate the correct position on the casualty's breastbone and be ready to start giving chest compression immediately after the second breath.

It is preferable that the two people work from opposite sides of the casualty (Fig. 6-23).

At the end of each series of five compressions, the person responsible for rescue breathing should be ready to give one breath without delay. It is helpful if the person giving the compressions counts aloud "one and two and three and four and five".

In two-person CPR, the casualty's head should be kept tilted and the chin lifted throughout. The person giving rescue breathing should maintain a clear airway, keep the chin lifted, and be ready to give one breath after each sequence of five compressions. As with single person CPR, each breath should take about $1\frac{1}{2}$ –2 seconds.

Chest compression should be continued as soon as the rescue breath has been delivered. There should be as little interruption to the cycle of compressions as possible.

The person giving chest compression can quickly become tired and so may wish to swap tasks with the person giving rescue breathing. This must be done as quickly and as smoothly as possible. The person giving chest compression should announce the change at the end of five compressions, then move rapidly to the casualty's head, check the airway, and give a single breath. During this manoeuvre, the other person should locate the correct point on the casualty's breastbone and get in position to start compressions as soon as the breath has been completed.

If both people become tired, other team members should take over. This must be done with as little interruption as possible to the rhythm. The take-over should be staggered, first one person being relieved then, once the rhythm has settled down again, the other.

FURTHER POINTS TO NOTE

The combination of chest compression and rescue breathing ensures that the casualty's blood is being artificially circulated and contains adequate amounts of oxygen.

Do not interrupt resuscitation until medical aid arrives and takes over. The only exception is if the casualty moves or takes a spontaneous breath. In this case, check the carotid pulse to see if the heart has started beating but take no more than ten seconds to do so. Even skilful CPR may not fully revive a casualty without other medical aid so time shouldn't be wasted by frequent checks for signs of a circulation.

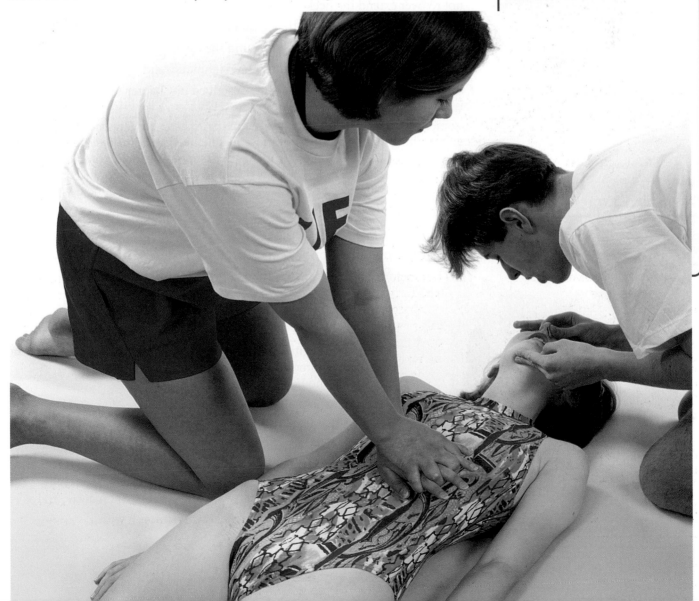

FIGURE 6-23
WORK FROM OPPOSITE SIDES.

Only a small amount of resistance should be felt during rescue breathing. Each breath should take about $1\frac{1}{2}$–2 seconds—any faster and the resistance will be greater with less air getting into the casualty's lungs.

The aim of rescue breathing is to breathe air into the casualty's lungs until their chest visibly rises. The person giving the breaths **must not** try to empty their own lungs completely.

Wait for the casualty's chest to fall as the air comes out before giving another breath. The exact timing is not critical — wait for the chest to fall and then give another breath.

Each compression should press the breastbone down about 4–5 cms and there should only be enough pressure applied to achieve this. The pressure should be firm, controlled and applied vertically. Any erratic or violent action will endanger the casualty. The casualty's chest should spend roughly equal times in the compressed and released phases.

The position of the hands on the breastbone is very important. Always check the position using the method described above.

PROBLEMS DURING RESUSCITATION

PROBLEMS WITH RESCUE BREATHING
If difficulty is experienced in inflating the casualty's chest:

- try to tilt the head further and increase the chin lift, taking care not to over extend the neck which can result in injury;
- check that the casualty's mouth is clear of any obstruction;
- make sure the lips are well sealed around the casualty's mouth;
- consider changing to the mouth-to-nose technique; and
- assess whether action for choking (as described in Chapter Seven) is needed.

In some circumstances (for instance, vomiting) it may be necessary to carry out rescue breathing using the mouth-to-nose technique. The casualty's mouth should be closed during the inflation and the lifeguard's mouth should completely cover the casualty's nose. The casualty's mouth should then open to let the breath out. Note that the nose may become blocked and there may be more difficulty in ensuring a clear airway.

During single person CPR it may be impracticable for the lifeguard to maintain held tilt as the compressions are being given. No specific action should be undertaken to maintain head tilt by any other means. It is difficult for the airway to be maintained during the compressions.

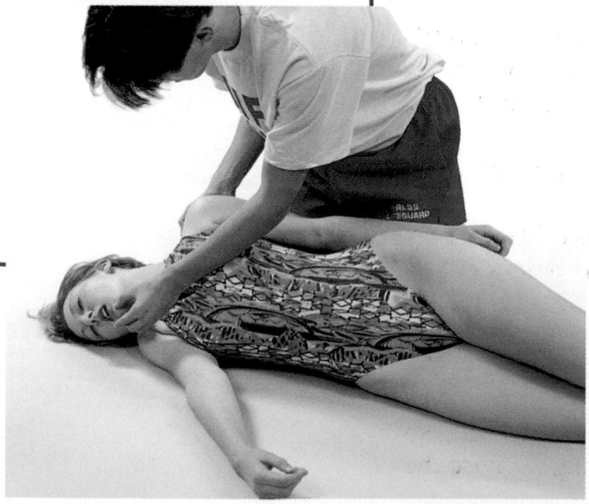

VOMITING
Vomiting may occur during or immediately after resuscitation. The danger is that the vomit will enter the air passages and lungs. This can interfere with breathing and also cause a particularly severe form of pneumonia. Immediate action is essential (Fig. 6-24). Lifeguards should:

- turn the casualty away from themselves;
- keep the casualty on the side;
- use the elbow and forearm to prevent the casualty rolling to a face down position;
- turn the casualty's head towards the floor with the mouth at the lowest point, allowing the vomit to drain away; and
- clear any debris from the casualty's mouth with the fingers.

FIGURE 6-24
ACTION FOR VOMITING.

Once vomiting has stopped and the mouth is clear of any debris, turn the casualty onto their back, re-establish the airway and continue rescue breathing at the normal rate.

AIR IN THE STOMACH

During rescue breathing, constriction of the airway may cause air to pass down the casualty's gullet into their stomach. As the stomach distends, it interferes with the downward movement of the diaphragm (the muscle at the base of the chest) and reduces inflation of the lungs. Air in the stomach also increases the risk of the casualty vomiting.

Swelling of the abdomen below the lower ribs indicates the stomach is distended. In this case, lifeguards should attempt to improve the casualty's airway by increasing head tilt and chin lift.

Lifeguards must **not** apply pressure to the casualty's stomach to expel the air because that will be very likely to induce vomiting. Provided a clear airway is maintained, the air in the stomach will usually escape gradually.

BROKEN RIBS

During chest compression one or more ribs may be heard to break. In elderly people, or those with particularly rigid chests, this may be unavoidable.

Broken ribs are far more likely if the force used to compress the chest is excessive, if the hands are incorrectly placed on the breastbone, or if the pressure is not applied directly downwards.

If a rib does break, no action can be taken during resuscitation, which should continue uninterrupted. After recovery the casualty may be in pain.

TRACHEOSTOMY

Very rarely, a lifeguard may have to resuscitate someone who has had a laryngectomy (an operation to remove their voice box). This leaves an opening in the windpipe at the front of the neck called a tracheostomy. Rescue breathing should be carried out by applying the mouth around the opening in the neck, ensuring a seal, and inflating the casualty's lungs in the usual way.

SPINAL INJURIES

Injury to the spine may be suspected if the casualty has fallen, been struck on the head or neck, or been rescued after diving into shallow water. Particular care must be taken to maintain alignment of the head, neck and chest during handling and resuscitation. Support and assistance from other team members will certainly be needed. Spinal injury management is covered in Chapter Eight.

RESUSCITATION OF COLD CASUALTIES

In cases of profound hypothermia (described in more detail in Chapter Seven), heartbeat is frequently slow and weak. Chest compressions should not be started unless no signs of a circulation are detected by looking for movement and feeling for the carotid pulse for about one minute.

If signs of a circulation are detected, there should be no further chest compressions while they are still present.

Effective CPR will have to be provided continuously until advanced life support can be provided by qualified and fully equipped medical aid. In practice, this means lifeguards will have to manage the casualty until the arrival of the emergency services.

If the casualty is not breathing, rescue breathing should be given as usual. The rates for both rescue breathing and chest compression should be the same as for other casualties. However, hypothermia may cause stiffness of the chest wall so there may be more resistance. The aim should be for rescue breathing to cause the chest to rise visibly.

RESUSCITATION IN THE WATER

Lifeguards should make every effort to bring casualties from deep water to a point of support before starting resuscitation. This may be at the edge of the pool or in shallow water where the lifeguard can stand on the pool bottom and support the casualty. It is virtually impossible to carry out chest compression on a casualty in the water because of the lack of support behind the casualty's back. Rescue breathing is possible while the lifeguard is swimming but requires a considerable degree of skill, a powerful swimming stroke and stamina.

If a casualty in deep water must be given rescue breathing, a torpedo buoy should be used to support the casualty.

If rescue breathing is carried out in the water, the mouth-to-nose technique is preferable because it allows the free arm to hold onto a support or pass behind the casualty's neck to assist head tilt.

To give rescue breathing while standing in water of no more than waist depth:

- support the casualty with one hand under their far armpit or between their shoulder blades;
- place the forearm under the casualty's neck to assist head tilt;
- remove any obstruction or loose dentures from the casualty's mouth;
- lift the casualty's chin;
- ensure water does not splash over the casualty's face; and
- give mouth-to-nose rescue breaths at the usual rate.

To give rescue breathing in water at a point of support such as the edge of the pool, pass one arm behind the casualty's neck and grip the pool side or other means of support. Use the other hand to obtain a chin lift, then proceed as above (Fig. 6-25).

Unless the casualty starts breathing at once, check for signs of a circulation (Fig. 6-26). If there are no signs, land the casualty as quickly as possible and start full cardio pulmonary resuscitation.

FIGURE 6-25
RESCUE BREATHING IN SHALLOW WATER.

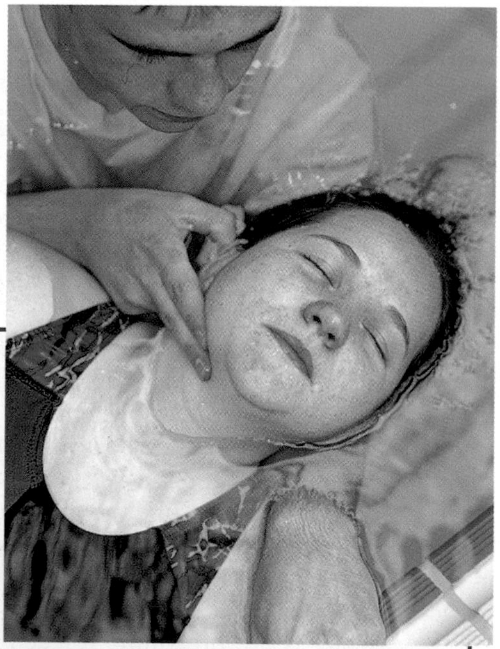

FIGURE 6-26
CHECK THE PULSE AT THE POOL SIDE.

RESUSCITATION USING SPECIALIST EQUIPMENT

There are three levels of resuscitation:

- **Basic Life Support** — CPR using rescue breathing and chest compression;
- **Basic Life Support With Adjuncts** — basic CPR plus use of face masks, suction equipment and oxygen; and
- **Advanced Life Support** — use of defibrillation equipment, oxygen supply apparatus and mechanical ventilators.

 RLSS UK RECOM-MENDS THAT ALL LIFEGUARDS WHO SUCCESSFULLY COMPLETE THE FOUNDATION MODULE OF THE NPLQ SHOULD EXTEND THEIR QUALIFICA-TION BY TRAINING FOR THE SEPARATE OXYGEN INSUFFLATION MODULE.

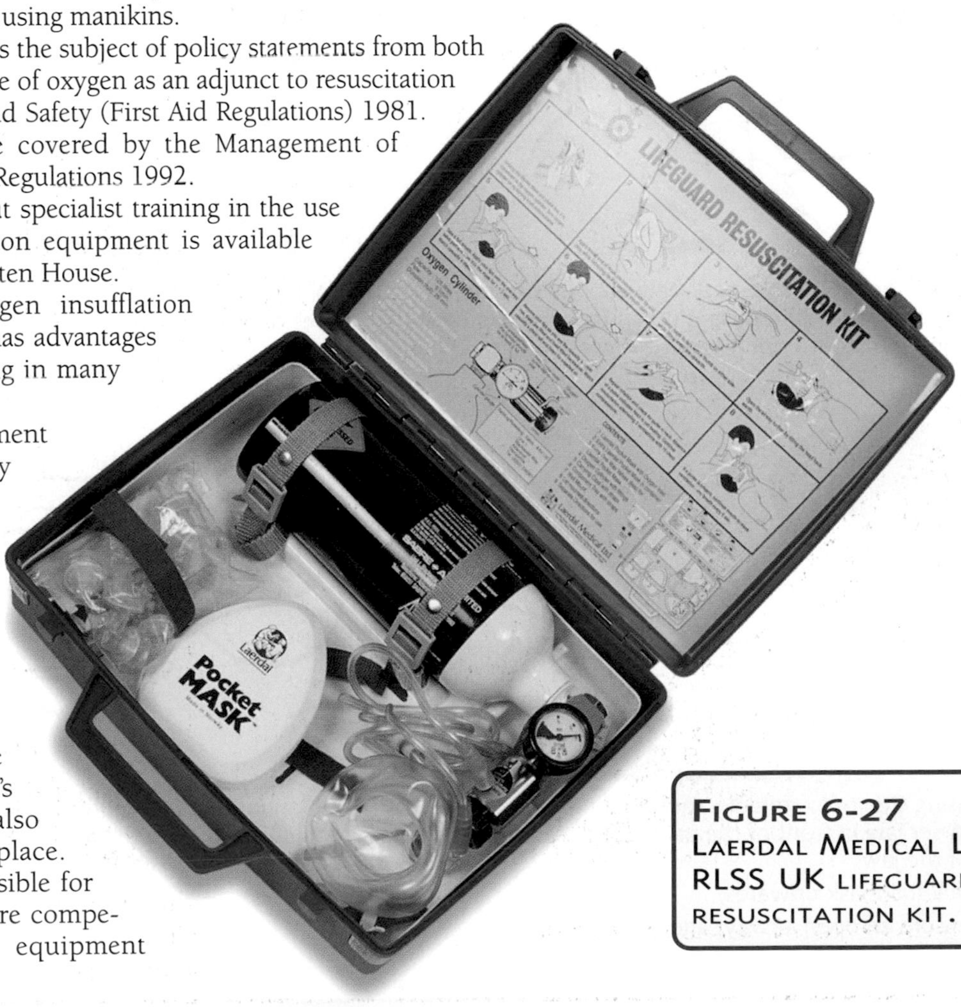

Specialist equipment is increasingly used as an adjunct to basic CPR so training in the use of pocket masks and other barrier devices is covered by the Foundation Module of the National Pool Lifeguard Qualification. However, the use of oxygen and defibrillation is **not** included in the Foundation Module.

The most common form of adjunct to CPR is the pocket mask or other barrier devices such as a plastic sheet with a valve orifice. It is essential when using these devices that a good air seal is maintained between the lifeguard and casualty. The casualty's head should remain tilted using the chin lift to ensure a clear airway.

If giving rescue breathing only, the lifeguard should work from a position at the top of the casualty's head. For rescue breathing combined with chest compression, the lifeguard should work from a position beside the casualty's head and have the mask strapped to the face. In this case it is better that a second trained lifeguard assists as noted in two-person CPR.

If no mask is immediately available, start mouth-to-mouth rescue breathing without delay.

Masks are reusable but must be thoroughly cleaned after use. The one-way valve must be discarded after use on a casualty. However, it can be cleaned and reused for training sessions using manikins.

Resuscitation equipment is the subject of policy statements from both RLSS UK and ISRM. The use of oxygen as an adjunct to resuscitation is covered by the Health and Safety (First Aid Regulations) 1981. Training requirements are covered by the Management of Health and Safety at Work Regulations 1992.

Further information about specialist training in the use of oxygen and defibrillation equipment is available from RLSS UK at Mountbatten House.

Resuscitation with oxygen insufflation (enriched air) equipment has advantages over basic rescue breathing in many cases (Fig. 6-27).

Under workplace equipment and health and safety legislation, all lifeguards having access to oxygen insufflation equipment must complete a training course and assessment before being permitted to use the equipment. The results of the assessment must be recorded in the lifeguard's Log Book and a record also retained at their workplace. Pool operators are responsible for ensuring that lifeguards are competent to use insufflation equipment where it is provided.

FIGURE 6-27
LAERDAL MEDICAL LTD. RLSS UK LIFEGUARD RESUSCITATION KIT.

POCKET MASK

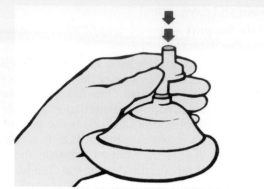

To use the Laerdal Medical Ltd Pocket Mask:
- remove the mask and valve from the container;
- push out the mask dome;

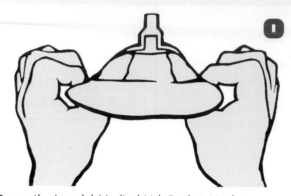

- mount the one way valve on the mask port;
- direct the exhalation port away from the lifeguard;

- place the rim of the mask between the casualty's lower lip and chin, pulling down the lower lip to keep the mouth open under the mask;

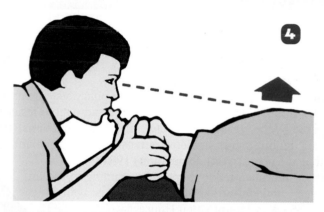

- hold the mask in place using both thumbs on the sides of the mask;

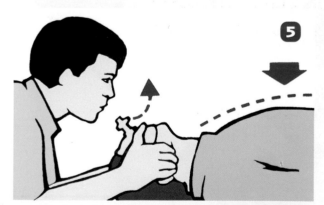

- using the index, middle and ring fingers grasp the lower jaw in front of the ear lobes above the angles of the jaw;
- pull the mask upwards;
- ensure an open airway; and
- give rescue breathing at the appropriate rate.

- On an infant, follow procedures described for adults and children except reverse the mask so that its nose part is under the chin.

TEST YOURSELF

1. What is the aim of resuscitation?

2. What do the terms respiration and circulation mean?

3. What two things are necessary to produce energy in the body?

4. Give an example of an involuntary movement.

5. Which organ is most vulnerable to lack of oxygen?

6. What does 'ABC' stand for in resuscitation?

7. What are the priorities when treating a casualty?

8. What is asphyxia?

9. Define drowning.

10. What does the word 'apnoea' mean?

11. Describe the difference between wet drowning and dry drowning.

12. What is hyperventilation?

13. What is secondary drowning?

14. What are the four stages in the chain of survival?

15. What do the terms 'cardio' and 'pulmonary' mean?

16. List the sequence of actions in resuscitation.

17. How would you check for signs of circulation?

18. Where can the carotid pulse be felt?

19. What is rescue breathing?

20. Describe how to locate the correct position on the breastbone for chest compression.

21. What is the ratio of rescue breaths to chest compressions for single person CPR?

22. What is the ratio for two-person CPR?

23. Is two-person CPR appropriate in the case of babies?

24. What problems are caused by vomiting and air in the stomach during CPR?

25. Describe how to give rescue breathing in the water.

26. What are the three levels of life support?

7

First Aid

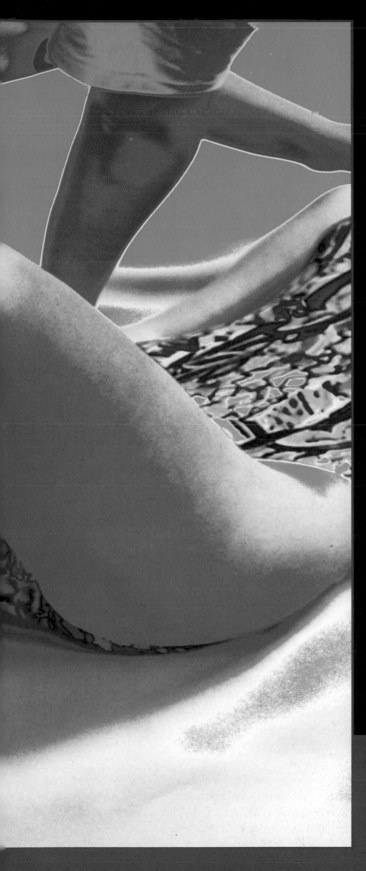

First Aid

FIRST AID is emergency help given to a casualty before qualified medical assistance arrives. First aid treatment by lifeguards should always be in accordance with the provisions of the pool's Normal Operating Procedures and Emergency Action Plan. Lifeguards should be familiar with the Health and Safety at Work First Aid Regulations 1981. The aims of first aid are:

- to preserve life;
- to minimise the effect of injury;
- to promote recovery; and
- to obtain further qualified medical assistance without delay.

The treatment notes for specific conditions and injuries later in this chapter are (with minor exceptions) in the same order as they appear in the syllabus of the Foundation Module of the National Pool Lifeguard Qualification.

ASSESSING CASUALTIES

After primary assessment (described in Chapter Six), lifeguards should conduct a secondary assessment by examining the casualty from head to extremities. Lifeguards should check:

- scalp for bumps, bruises, indentations, bleeding;
- eyes for injury or bleeding;
- ears for bleeding, fluid, bruising;
- nose for bleeding, fluid, other damage;
- cheek for temperature, colour, clamminess, swelling, or damaged cheekbone;
- mouth for obstruction, foreign objects, fluid, vomit, tongue laceration, broken teeth, loose dentures, damage to jawbone;
- breathing for regularity, rate, unusual odour;
- neck for damage, deformity, carotid pulse, distended veins, bleeding, swelling;
- chest and back for rise and fall, bruises, deformity, swelling, chest wounds, flail chest, back pain, compression pain;
- abdomen for rigidity, tenderness, bruising, bleeding, bowel protrusion, bowel or bladder discharge, incontinence, pelvic girdle compression pain;
- limbs and extremities (legs first, then arms) for bruises, discoloration, swelling, deformity, broken bones or bone protrusion, bleeding, joint mobility, dislocation, circulation, reaction to stimuli, needle marks, Medic Alert bracelet.

As well as examining casualties for the signs listed above, lifeguards should ask casualties to describe any pains or other symptoms.

Note that injuries to the neck and spine can lead to paralysis if the casualty is not treated and handled correctly. Spinal injuries are covered in Chapter Eight.

REMOVING CLOTHING

Sometimes it may be necessary to remove a casualty's clothing to diagnose and treat injuries. This should be done with minimum disturbance, removing only as much clothing as necessary. Take care not to damage clothing if this can be avoided. If the casualty is conscious, they should be told what is being done and why.

If underclothing must be removed, there should be a witness present. Removal of valuables such as watches or jewellery should also be witnessed and the objects carefully safeguarded.

FIRST AID

The aims of first aid are:
- to preserve life;
- to minimise the effect of injury;
- to promote recovery; and
- to obtain further qualified medical assistance without delay.

HYGIENE MEASURES

When dealing with casualties, lifeguards should wear protective gloves if possible (Fig. 7-1). A typical lifeguard uniform offers little protection, so protective aprons are also recommended.

Lifeguards must always wash their hands thoroughly with soap and water before and after attending wounds. They should cover any exposed cuts or breaks in their own skin with a waterproof dressing.

After contact with blood or other body fluids, lifeguards should wash as soon as possible with soap and running water. If the lips, mouth, tongue or eyes are contaminated, they should be rinsed with copious amounts of running water.

Avoid touching the casualty's wound or any part of a dressing which might contact the wound. Never talk or cough over a wound or a dressing.

Mop up spills of blood or other body fluids then disinfect using one part household bleach diluted in ten parts water. Contaminated clothing should be cleaned in a washing machine on a hot washing cycle.

Place all used dressings or infected material in a plastic bag, seal and label it and incinerate it. Disposable paper towels should be used if possible and incinerated afterwards (Fig. 7-2).

Place any needles or sharp items in a sealed tin and dispose of them according to the provisions of the NOP or EAP.

Advice about hygiene management can be obtained from local health authorities, the Employment Medical Advisory Service (EMAS) or from the Health and Safety Executive. RLSS UK publishes guidance on the question of HIV and rescue breathing.

DIAGNOSIS AND RECORDING

Diagnosis means identifying the cause of an illness or the nature of an injury from the casualty's signs or symptoms observed during primary or secondary assessment. Symptoms are that of which a casualty complains. Signs are what a lifeguard finds during examination.

For instance, assessment might reveal swelling of the ankle and an inability to move the toes. These are signs. The cause might be severe bruising, a sprain, dislocation or a fracture. Deciding the cause is diagnosis.

Lifeguards need to be trained to diagnose conditions they are likely to encounter. This skill comes from initial and in-service training, from dealing with both real and simulated emergencies and from experience.

In making a diagnosis, it helps to know the history of the event or how the accident occurred. If casualties are conscious, lifeguards can ask them for the information. If casualties are unconscious, lifeguards should ask witnesses or bystanders, note the position of the casualties, and look for known medical factors such as information on a Medic Alert bracelet.

It is also very important to record the condition of the casualty. This record may be needed in a subsequent report. More importantly, it can be of great help to qualified medical practitioners who later take over the care of the casualty.

The basic information should include:

- how the accident occurred;
- if the casualty is, or has been, unconscious and for how long;
- the pulse rate and its character;
- details of injuries and any blood loss;
- details of any treatment given and at what time; and
- details of the person dealing with the casualty.

Recording the state of the casualty at the scene of an accident is very important. The information which will be required by anyone taking over care of a casualty should be entered on an observation chart. A reproduction of a widely used observation chart appears on the following page.

FIGURE 7-1
USE PROTECTIVE GLOVES WHEN TREATING WOUNDS.

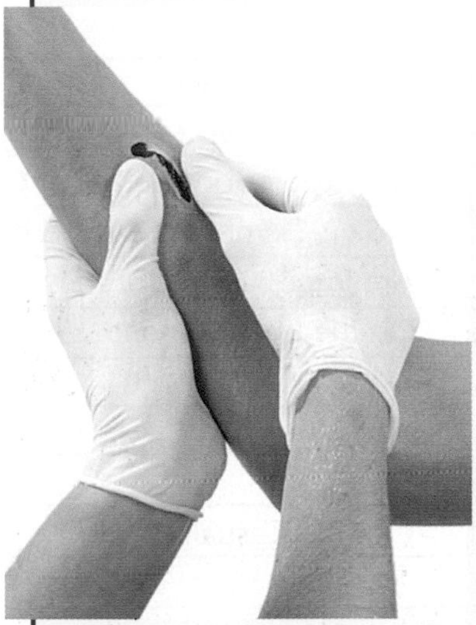

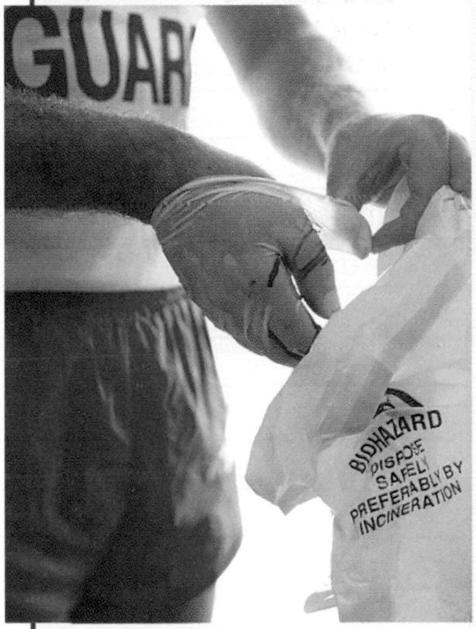

FIGURE 7-2
DISPOSING OF SOILED GLOVES AND OTHER ITEMS.

OBSERVATION CHART

Casualty Name:

Date:

Time in Minutes		10	20	30	40	50
Is Skin Flushed / Pale / Blue? F / P / B						
Is Body Hot or Cold? H or C						
Is Skin Clammy or Dry? C or D						
Are Pupils Dilated or Regular? Y or N						
Do the Eyes Respond…?	Spontaneously					
	To Speech					
	To Pain					
	Not at All					
Can the Casualty Speak?	Normally					
	Confusedly					
	Incomprehensibly					
	Not at All					
Can the Casualty Move?	On Command					
	To Painful Stimulus					
	Not at All					
Pulse	Faster					
(Beats per Minute)	121–130					
	111–120					
	101–110					
	91–100					
	81–90					
	71–80					
	61–70					
	51–60					
	Slower					
Is Pulse Regular?	Y / N					
Is Pulse Strong/Weak/Normal?	S / W / N					
Respiration?	Faster					
(Breaths per Minute)	71–80					
	61–70					
	51–60					
	41–50					
	31–40					
	21–30					
	11–20					
	1–10					

FIGURE 7-3
PLACE CASUALTY IN RECOVERY POSITION

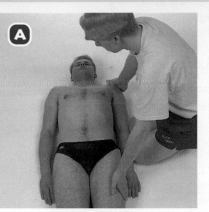

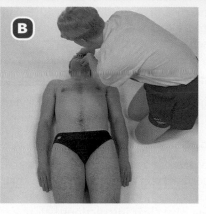

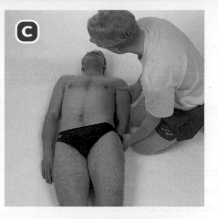

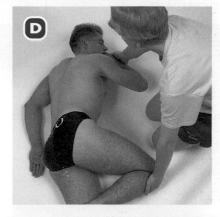

- Kneel beside the casualty and make sure that both legs are straight (Fig. 7-3 A)
- Open the casualty's airway by tilting the head and lifting the chin (Fig. 7-3 B).
- Tuck the hand nearest to you under the thigh, keeping the casualty's arm straight and palm uppermost (Fig. 7-3 C).
- Bring the casualty's far arm across the chest and hold the back of the hand across the cheek.
- Grasp the casualty's far leg just above the knee and pull it up, keeping the foot on the ground.
- Keeping the hand pressed against the cheek, pull on the far leg to roll the casualty onto the side (Fig. 7-3 D).
- Adjust the casualty's upper leg so that both hips or knee are bent at right angles.
- Adjust the lower arm so that the casualty is not lying on it and the palm is still uppermost (Fig. 7-3 E).
- Tilt the casualty's head back to make sure the airway remains open.
- Adjust the casualty's hand under her cheek, if necessary, and keep the head tilted.
- Check the casualty's breathing.

A STRAIGHTEN LEGS.
B OPEN AIRWAY.
C TUCK ARM UNDER THIGH.
D PULL ON FAR LEG.
E COMPLETED RECOVERY POSITION.

THE RECOVERY POSITION

An unconscious casualty whose airway is clear and who is breathing spontaneously should be turned into the recovery position. This prevents the tongue falling back to block the airway and reduces the risk of vomit getting into the lungs.

If there are other injuries, the recovery position may need to be modified. If spinal injury is suspected, casualties must be handled with great care and their head supported and kept in line with their spine (refer to Chapter Eight).

When casualties are placed in the recovery position awaiting the arrival of qualified medical aid, at least one lifeguard or trained first aider must stay with them and watch for signs of deterioration, especially in the early stages after resuscitation. If casualties are conscious, gentle reassurance can be very comforting and may help to reduce the risk of shock.

If the casualty is clothed, loosen or remove any constricting or bulky items. Remove spectacles if worn. To place a casualty into the recovery position, follow the procedure above.

MOVING AND HANDLING CASUALTIES

Never move an ill or injured person unless their life is endangered or there is some other very urgent need to move them. It is better to leave the casualty undisturbed, summon medical aid and provide first aid on the spot.

If the casualty's safety is at risk (for instance, from drowning, poisonous gas or fire) move them as quickly and carefully as possible without endangering them or yourself.

The method used to move a casualty will depend on:

- the nature and severity of any injuries;
- the number of team members or helpers available;
- the casualty's weight; and
- the distance to be covered.

Never move a seriously injured casualty alone unless no help is available and the danger is acute. Always make sure that everyone involved, including the casualty (if conscious), knows exactly what is going to happen and what they must do. Always give clear instructions before each movement.

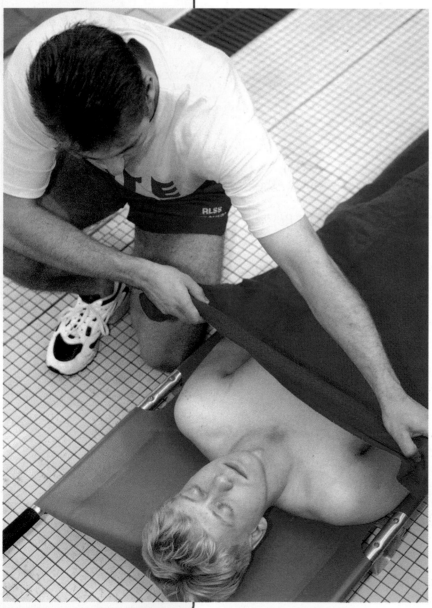

FIGURE 7-4
PREPARING A CASUALTY FOR REMOVAL TO MEDICAL AID.

AFTERCARE

Unless an injury has been of a very minor nature, qualified medical assistance must be obtained from a doctor or by transferring the casualty to hospital (Fig. 7-4).

Lifeguards must give as much information as possible to ambulance crews or other medical practitioners who take over care of the casualty. This information contributes greatly to further treatment. The observation chart described earlier in this chapter can play a very importance role in subsequent care of the casualty.

Regardless of how well casualties appear to be recovering, lifeguards should seek further qualified medical aid if they are in any doubt. They must always seek medical aid if:

- the casualty has been unconscious;
- any form of resuscitation has been necessary;
- there are any signs of shock; or
- the casualty has been submerged (near drowning).

FIRST AID BOXES

A first aid box should be clearly identified with a white cross on a green background. It should contain nothing other than first aid materials and only contain items which lifeguards have been trained to use.

The contents should be replenished as soon as possible after use. Items should not be used after their expiry date. The box should protect the contents from damp and dirt.

Details of the contents of first aid boxes are contained in the Health and Safety at Work First Aid Regulations 1981. The regulations say that no drugs should be contained in a first aid box (Fig. 7-5).

DRESSINGS AND BANDAGES

A dressing is a protective covering which is placed on a wound to control bleeding, prevent infection and absorb any discharge (Fig. 7-6). Dressings should be sterile, absorbent, and large enough to extend beyond the area of the wound. Small self adhesive dressings are commonly known as 'plasters'.

Sterile dressings must not be used if the seal of the pack they come in is broken.

Applying dressings

Always place dressings directly onto a wound, never slide them on from the side. If bleeding is under control, clean the wound and surrounding skin before applying the dressing. If necessary to absorb discharge, cover dressings with sterile pads of cotton held in position by a bandage. If a dressing slips off before it can be secured, replace it in case it has picked up infection from the surrounding skin.

If the wound has a foreign object in it, the dressing should not come into direct contact with the object.

Triangular bandages

Triangular bandages can be used open or unfolded as a sling to support or protect the arms or chest. They can be used to secure dressings on the head, hands and feet, and also be folded according to specific needs.

A triangular bandage can be made by cutting diagonally in half a piece of linen or calico not less than 1 metre square. The illustration shows how to fold a triangular bandage.

Slings provide support and protection for injured arms, wrists and hands or for immobilising limbs. There are two types, the arm sling and the elevated sling.

Applying an arm sling (Fig. 7-7)

With the casualty sitting down, support the forearm on the injured side. Sometimes, the casualty can support their own arm.

Using the natural hollow between the elbow and the chest, slide one end of the open triangular bandage between the chest and the forearm. The point should stretch beyond the elbow on the injured side.

Place the upper end over the shoulder on the uninjured side and around the back on the injured side. Supporting the forearm, carry the lower end of the bandage up over the forearm and hand, leaving only the fingertips exposed.

Tie off with a reef knot at the hollow above the collar bone on the injured side.

Bring the point forward and secure it to the front of the bandage with a safety pin or tuck it in between the bandage and the forearm. Ensure that the casualty's circulation is not restricted by the sling by, for instance, checking the colour and temperature of their fingers.

Applying an elevated sling (Fig. 7-8)

Support the casualty's forearm on the injured side across their chest with their fingers resting on their opposite shoulder. Place the triangular bandage over their arm and hand, the point of the bandage extended below the elbow and the upper end of the bandage over the shoulder.

Gently place the base of the bandage under the forearm and secure it with a safety pin. Ensure that the casualty's circulation is not restricted by the sling.

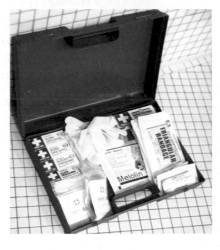

FIGURE 7-5
A TYPICAL FIRST AID BOX.

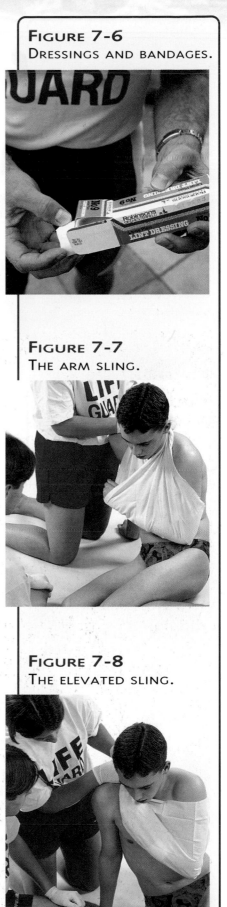

FIGURE 7-6
DRESSINGS AND BANDAGES.

FIGURE 7-7
THE ARM SLING.

FIGURE 7-8
THE ELEVATED SLING.

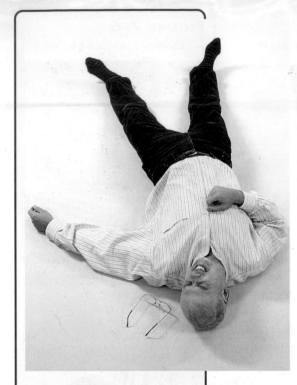

FIGURE 7-9
A COLLAPSED CASUALTY.

UNCONSCIOUSNESS, FAINTING AND HEAD INJURIES

UNCONSCIOUSNESS

Among other causes, loss of consciousness can be due to:

- reduced supply of blood to the brain from suffocation, heart attack, stroke or shock;
- head injury;
- poisoning or drugs;
- effects of extremes of temperature;
- near drowning;
- epilepsy or diabetes.

Diagnosis

Disturbance of consciousness may vary from slight drowsiness or confusion to a deep coma in which the casualty is totally unresponsive. In first aid, a simple distinction between consciousness and unconsciousness may be made by gently shaking the casualty and calling 'are you awake' or something similar. When doing this, care should be taken to cause as little movement as possible so that any injury, particularly to the neck, is not aggravated.

Treatment

Alert the lifeguard team and make sure someone has summoned an ambulance or other qualified medical aid in accordance with the EAP. Casualties who have suffered any disturbance of consciousness must be transferred to hospital for further observation.

It is important to handle unconscious casualties with great care, particularly their heads. Do not leave an unconscious casualty unattended but maintain observation of them. Lifeguards should:

- remove or treat any obvious immediate cause of unconsciousness;
- ensure the casualty has a clear airway (as described in Chapter Six);
- examine the casualty and treat any serious injuries;
- control any major bleeding;
- start rescue breathing immediately if the casualty's breathing weakens or stops;
- place the casualty in the recovery position if breathing is normal (taking care not to aggravate any injury, especially suspected spinal injury);
- loosen the casualty's clothing at the neck, chest and waist;
- protect the casualty from cold and wet; and
- record any changes in condition and pass on the information to qualified medical practitioners when they take over care of the casualty.

If consciousness returns, reassure the casualty but do not give anything to eat or drink.

FAINTING

Fainting follows a temporary reduction of the blood supply to the brain. It may begin with a feeling of dizziness and lead to collapse (Fig. 7-9). Causes of fainting include:

- injuries;
- illness;
- fatigue; and
- long periods in a hot stuffy atmosphere.

Diagnosis

The casualty may yawn, sway and become unsteady and giddy. The face may become pale and there may be sweat on the face, neck and hands. Consciousness may be clouded.

In a full faint, the casualty may be unconscious, the face may be pale and the skin cold and clammy. The casualty's breathing may be shallow. The pulse may be weak and slow initially, but may gradually increase in rate.

Treatment

For an impending faint, reassure the casualty, advise them to breathe deeply but slowly, lay them down in a current of fresh air or sit them down and lower their head between their knees. Loosen any tight clothing.

Upon recovery the casualty may be given sips of water. No alcohol must be given.

In a full faint, lay the casualty down with the legs raised and ensure an open airway. If the casualty does not come round quickly, place them in the recovery position and summon medical aid.

HEAD INJURIES

Head injuries can damage the brain, leading to dizziness, confusion and unconsciousness. Concussion or compression injury to the brain may result and a full and thorough examination of the casualty is essential.

Head injuries are usually caused by falls, banging the head on overhead objects or by diving into shallow water.

Direct blows to the head may cause scalp wounds or bruising. The skull may be fractured, possibly with little external evidence of damage.

Concussion leads to widespread but temporary disturbance of the brain. There may be dizziness or nausea, loss of short term memory about the events surrounding the accident and a mild generalised headache.

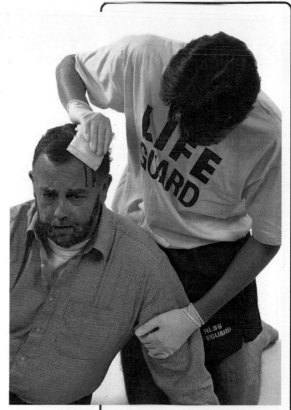

FIGURE 7-10
TREATING A HEAD
INJURY WITH PAD
AND BANDAGE.

Treatment

If the casualty is rendered unconscious by a head injury, alert the lifeguard team, summon urgent medical aid and follow the guidelines for handling unconscious casualties.

If the casualty is conscious, treat any cuts or bruising (Fig. 7-10). If concussion is suspected, keep a careful watch for signs of change in the level of consciousness, even after apparent recovery, and transfer the casualty to hospital.

Lifeguards should always seek qualified medical aid for casualties with head injuries.

HEART ATTACK, CHOKING, AND SHOCK

HEART ATTACK

A heart attack occurs if one of the coronary arteries supplying blood to the heart suddenly becomes blocked. Cardiac arrest can result. (See Fig. 7-11 on next page.)

Diagnosis

If the casualty is conscious, they will complain of severe, crushing, tight pain in the centre of the chest which may spread to the arms, throat and back.

The casualty will look pale and sweaty with signs of shock. Breathing may become difficult. They may feel giddy and sink to the ground and may become unconscious. Their circulation will become weak and their pulse may be irregular or fail.

HEART ATTACK AND CHOKING

Heart attack:

- Casualty may sit down and be quiet
- Casualty may hold their central chest
- Casualty often complains of chest pain
- Face may be blue but is often pale
- Breathing is usually rapid and quiet.

Choking:

- Casualty may stand up and be agitated
- Casualty may clutch their neck or throat
- There is no chest pain
- Face is blue
- Breathing may be noisy or absent.

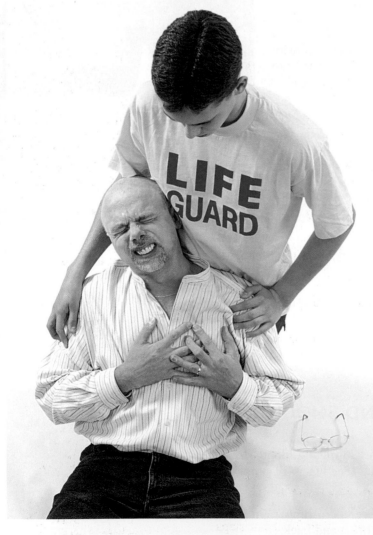

FIGURE 7-11
A SUSPECTED HEART ATTACK.

It is important to distinguish between a casualty who is suffering a heart attack and one who is choking. Sometimes the two conditions can be confused with one another (see panel at left).

Treatment
Alert the lifeguard team and immediately summon qualified medical aid. If casualties are in the water, they will be unable to continue swimming and may clutch their chest and show signs of severe distress. They may become unconscious, either sinking or remaining on the surface.

Lifeguards must take immediate action to remove the casualty from the water, not only to prevent drowning but because water in the casualty's airway will further complicate an already serious situation. The rescue must be conducted with care.

Once the casualty is out of the water (or if they have suffered the heart attack on land), place them in a half-sitting, half-lying position and loosen any constriction around their neck and the waist (Fig. 7-11).

Reassure the casualty while checking their breathing and circulation. If the casualty becomes unconscious but continues breathing, place them in the recovery position and monitor their condition. Be prepared to start cardio pulmonary resuscitation if the casualty's circulation fails.

CHOKING
Choking occurs when vomit, a piece of food or other material is swallowed but goes down the windpipe rather than the gullet thus obstructing the airway.

If the obstruction is only partial, the casualty will usually be able to dislodge it by coughing but if there is complete obstruction to the flow of air this may not be possible. Even a small item may cause serious obstruction because its presence can lead to muscle spasm and this can close the airway.

Without help, the casualty will suffer suffocation, become unconscious and may die.

Diagnosis
The casualty may have been seen eating, putting an object into their mouth, or vomiting.

Choking casualties often grip their throat with their hand. If the airway is only partially obstructed, casualties will be distressed and coughing and their breathing may be noisy and wheezy. If the airway is completely obstructed, they will be unable to speak, breathe or cough. Their face may become blue with the veins standing out in the neck.

Treatment
If the casualty is breathing, encourage them to continue coughing but do nothing else.

If the casualty shows signs of becoming weak or stops breathing or coughing, leave them in the position in which you find them, remove any obvious debris or loose dentures from the mouth and carry out back slapping.

If the casualty is standing or sitting, the procedure for back slapping is:

- stand to the side and slightly behind the casualty;
- support the casualty's chest with one hand and lean them well forward; and
- give up to five sharp slaps between the casualty's shoulder blades with the heel of the hand (Fig. 7-12).

If the casualty is lying down, the procedure for back slapping is:

- kneel beside the casualty;
- roll the casualty towards you on their side;
- support their chest with your thigh; and
- give up to five sharp slaps between the casualty's shoulder blades with the heel of the hand (Fig. 7-13).

The aim is to relieve the obstruction with each slap so it may not be necessary to give all five.

If back slapping fails, try giving abdominal thrusts. This technique forces air out of the windpipe by a sudden inward and upward movement of the diaphragm. The technique can be used whether the casualty is standing, sitting or lying.

Abdominal thrusts must **not** be given to babies (see below).

If the casualty is standing or sitting, make sure they are bending well forwards so that when the obstructing object is dislodged it comes out of the mouth rather than goes further down the airway. To give abdominal thrusts:

- stand behind the casualty and put both arms round the upper part of their abdomen;
- clench your fist and place it just below the point where the lower ribs meet and grasp it with your other hand; and
- pull sharply inwards and upwards.

If the casualty is lying on the ground, turn them onto their back if necessary. To give abdominal thrusts:

- kneel astride the casualty;
- place the heel of one hand in the upper part of the casualty's abdomen where the lower ribs meet; and
- place the other hand on top and push sharply towards the casualty's head (Fig. 7-14).

If the obstruction is still not relieved, continue alternating five back slaps with five abdominal thrusts.

When giving back slaps to a baby or child, it may be easier to support the casualty on your knee. It is important to make sure that the head is lower than the chest to make sure that the dislodged object comes out of the mouth.

FIGURE 7-12
ASSISTING WHILE STANDING.

FIGURE 7-13
ASSISTING WHILE ON THE GROUND.

FIGURE 7-14
ABDOMINAL THRUST.

STEPS FOR TREATING CHOKING CHILDREN

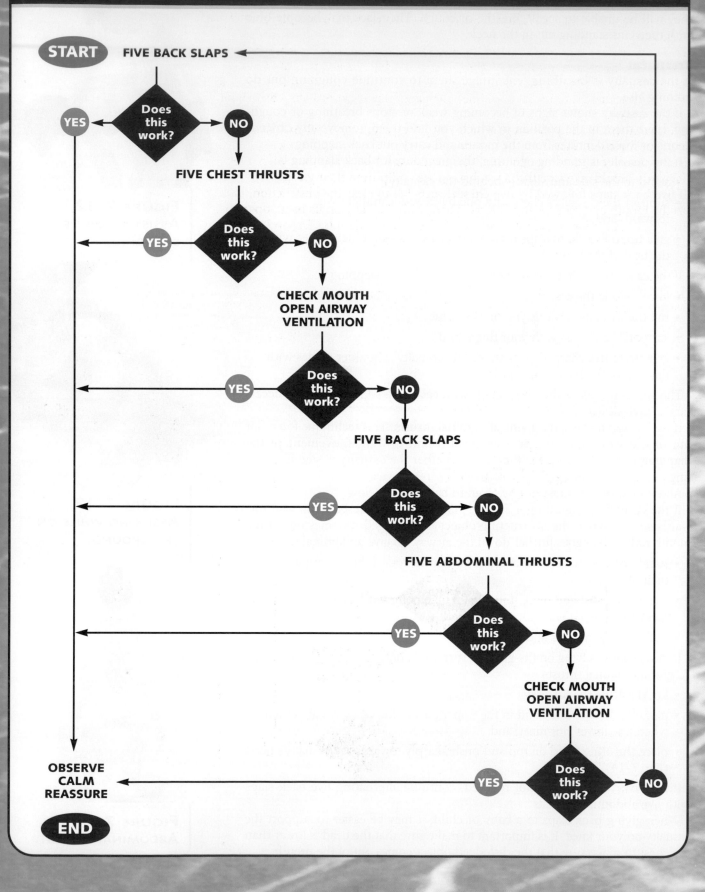

TREATING CHOKING BABIES

It is dangerous to give abdominal thrusts to babies. Instead, if five back slaps fail to relieve the obstruction, give five chest thrusts. These are similar to the chest compressions described in Chapter Six and are given at the same place on the breastbone.

It is important not to confuse chest thrusts for choking with the chest compressions for cardio pulmonary resuscitation. The main difference is that for choking, each individual thrust is given to relieve the obstruction, rather than as part of a series of five. The chest thrust should be sharp and more vigorous and carried out at a slower rate.

Babies may be lifted by their legs or laid along the arm or thigh when giving back slaps, but for chest thrusts it is important that babies are on their back on a firm surface (which could be the thigh). Their head should be lower than their chest. Lifeguards should take care that a wet baby doesn't slip from their grasp.

If five back slaps followed by five chest thrusts fail to clear the obstruction, look into the mouth and remove any objects. Then, with the baby on its back, open the airway by means of the head tilt and chin lift described in Chapter Six, and attempt to give a rescue breath. If this cannot be done, repeat the sequence of back slaps and chest thrusts.

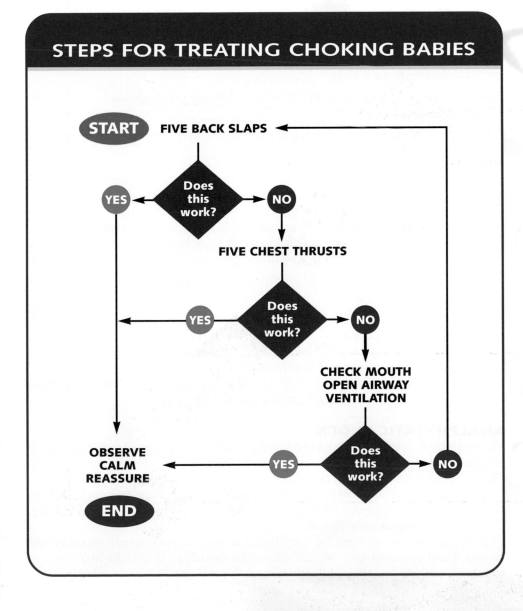

STEPS FOR TREATING CHOKING BABIES

START — FIVE BACK SLAPS
Does this work? — YES / NO
NO → FIVE CHEST THRUSTS
Does this work? — YES / NO
NO → CHECK MOUTH / OPEN AIRWAY / VENTILATION
Does this work? — YES / NO
YES → OBSERVE / CALM / REASSURE → END

SHOCK

The medical definition of shock has very little to do with the popular use of the word (although fear and emotion may make the condition worse). Medically, shock is very serious and requires urgent qualified medical attention. Casualties suffering from shock should be transferred to hospital as soon as possible.

Shock can be defined as failure of the circulation which results in an inadequate supply of blood to vital organs.

Shock occurs when there is not enough blood being pumped round the body. Causes of shock include:

- loss of blood due to external or internal bleeding;
- loss of fluid from burns, severe vomiting, diarrhoea or profuse sweating;
- heart failure, heart attack or severe irregularity of the heart beat;
- certain virus infections;
- blood infections;
- severe pain or injury; and
- near-drowning.

Failure of the circulation means that essential parts of the body such as the brain, kidneys and heart do not receive as much oxygen as they need and can no longer function properly. Unless casualties are treated quickly they may die. The body tries to compensate for the lack of circulating blood by:

- drawing the remaining blood away from the skin and directing it to more important areas;
- increasing the rate of breathing to get as much oxygen as possible into the blood; and
- speeding up the heart to circulate the blood more rapidly.

CASUALTIES SUFFERING FROM SHOCK SHOULD BE TRANSFERRED TO HOSPITAL AS SOON AS POSSIBLE. REMEMBER, SHOCK IS POTENTIALLY FATAL.

Diagnosis

The signs of shock result from lack of oxygen and the body's compensating action. The brain is most affected by reduced blood supply so casualties in shock feel faint, dizzy and confused. In severe cases they may become unconscious.

As blood is drawn away, the skin becomes pale and cold to the touch. Sweating often accompanies shock. The pulse is rapid but weak because the reduced volume of blood in the arteries results in low blood pressure. Breathing is rapid and the casualty seems to be gasping for air.

Treatment

Treat the causes of the shock if possible — for example, by stopping external bleeding or dressing burns. Lay conscious casualties flat with their legs raised. Reassure the casualty. Unconscious casualties should be placed in the recovery position. Keep casualties warm to prevent heat loss.

Do not give casualties food or drink because this may cause vomiting with its attendant risk of stomach contents getting into the lungs.

ANALPHYLATIC SHOCK

This is a serious, potentially fatal condition caused by a massive allergic reaction. In sensitive casualties, analphylatic shock can develop within a few seconds or minutes following an insect sting, eating certain food or taking certain drugs.

There may be symptoms of shock, anxiety, swelling of the face and neck, blotchy skin, puffiness around the eyes, impaired breathing, rapid pulse and nausea. Unconsciousness may soon follow.

Qualified medical aid must be summoned at once if analphylatic shock is suspected. Until specialist help arrives, conscious casualties should sit in a position which relieves any breathing difficulties.

POISONING, ELECTRIC SHOCK, TEMPERATURE EFFECTS

POISONING

Lifeguards may encounter poisoning. In a swimming pool, it is most likely to result from drug or alcohol poisoning, or from industrial chemicals or gases.

Poisons can enter the body through the mouth, the nose, by injection or by absorption through the skin. Casualties may be conscious or unconscious.

Drug poisoning may result from both recreational use of illegal drugs or by accidental or deliberate misuse of legitimate medication. The condition may be complicated by other intoxicants or the health of the casualty.

The wide range of possible drug poisoning makes diagnosis difficult. Lifeguards should alert the lifeguard team and summon qualified medical aid immediately. They should maintain observation of the casualty, taking particular care to monitor breathing and circulation.

Alcohol poisoning can occur if a pool user enters the premises intoxicated or becomes intoxicated while there. Lifeguards must be vigilant in looking for signs of alcohol use and be aware of the possibility of drinkers collapsing because of intoxication.

In cases of alcohol poisoning, lifeguards should alert the lifeguard team and summon qualified medical aid immediately. They should maintain observation of the casualty, taking particular care to monitor breathing and circulation.

Industrial chemicals or gases

Although uncommon, lifeguards may have to deal with a spillage or release of toxic chemicals or gas (Fig. 7-15). This may come from the pool's plant room or chemical store. Safety precautions detailed in the EAP or by the manufacturers must always be followed and lifeguards should be familiar with the Control of Substances Hazardous to Health Regulations and the guidance issued by the Institute of Sport and Recreation Management.

In all cases of industrial gas and chemical leakage, qualified medical aid and the fire brigade should be summoned in accordance with the EAP. The firefighters and medical practitioners will need to be told what type of fumes or chemicals they are dealing with.

FIGURE 7-15
INDUSTRIAL CHEMICALS AND GASES CAN BE DANGEROUS.

If casualties are in a closed space where the presence of poisonous fumes is suspected, no attempt at rescue should be made unless lifeguards have breathing apparatus and are trained in its use. Rescuers must have support from other team members. Doors and windows should be opened where this is possible without endangering anyone or contaminating other parts of the premises.

Treatment

Never attempt resuscitation in a smoke or gas filled room. Remove the casualties to a safe place.

Check the casualty's breathing and circulation and be prepared to start cardio pulmonary resuscitation. If rescue breathing is needed, lifeguards should be very careful not to inhale the casualty's exhaled breath. It may be necessary for the person giving rescue breathing to move their head right away from the casualty's head between breaths.

If the casualty is unconscious but breathing normally, put them in the recovery position.

FIGURE 7-16
ELECTRIC SHOCK CASES NEED CAREFUL EMERGENCY ACTION.

ELECTRIC SHOCK

Lifeguards are unlikely to encounter electric shock victims because low voltage power supplies are used in swimming pools and governed by the Electricity at Work Regulations 1989 and the Workplace (Health, Safety and Welfare) Regulations 1992. Dealing with electrical emergencies must be undertaken in accordance with the EAP.

Contact with electricity can result in:

• unconsciousness (Fig. 7-16);

• spasm of the respiratory muscles so that breathing stops (the most common cause of death in cases of electric shock);

• cardiac arrest due to ventricular fibrillation; and

• burns at the point(s) of contact.

It is essential that the electrical contact with the casualty is broken before anyone touches them for rescue or treatment. To break the contact, switch off the power supply, remove the appropriate plug or wrench cables away if it is safe to do so.

If none of these are possible, stand on dry insulating material such as a rubber mat, wood or thick newspaper and use a piece of non-conducting material, such as a broom handle, to push the casualty out of contact with the power source.

High voltage supply may be found in plant rooms. If a casualty is found in contact with high voltage no rescue should be attempted until a qualified authority confirms that the power supply has been turned off.

Treatment

Once casualties are not in contact with the electrical source, check for breathing and circulation. Start cardio pulmonary resuscitation if necessary. If casualties are unconscious but breathing, place them in the recovery position.

Look for signs of shock and for localised burns and treat accordingly.

If casualties have been unconscious or if they appear shaken, qualified medical aid should be sought immediately.

HEAT EXHAUSTION AND SUNBURN

Heat exhaustion usually develops gradually and results from loss of salt and water from the body by excessive sweating. It commonly afflicts people who are unfit or unaccustomed to physical activity.

Casualties may complain of headaches, dizziness or confusion and may be sweating with a rapid, weakening pulse.

Treatment

Move the casualty a cool place. Lay them down with their legs raised. Do not allow them to become too cold. They should sip a solution of one teaspoon of salt in a litre of water. If recovery is rapid, advise the casualty to see a doctor.

If the casualty becomes unconscious, place them in the recovery position, alert the lifeguard team and summon medical aid. Keep them under observation and check their breathing and circulation.

Sunburn

Lifeguards are unlikely to encounter sunburn except at open air lidos. They must protect themselves from sunburn and advise pool users how to avoid it.

The signs of sunburn are redness, itching, and tenderness of the skin. In some cases the skin will blister. When combined with windy conditions, wetness or sweat, sunburn can cause serious burns.

Treatment

Move the casualty to shade, give sips of cold water and treat for the effects of over heating. Seek medical aid if the burning is severe.

HYPOTHERMIA

The medical definition of hypothermia is when a casualty's core body temperature falls below 35°C. Even if the drop in temperature is not as much as this, casualties may still suffer ill effects. The very old and very young are particularly vulnerable to cold.

Core body temperature will drop if the rate of heat lost from the body exceeds that being produced. Heat production can be impaired by exhaustion, intoxication from drugs and alcohol, or where injury or accident causes immobilisation.

Lifeguards are unlikely to encounter hypothermia in indoor pools although in some locations, especially during the winter, customers may get very cold if they go in and out of the water over a long period.

Evacuation of a pool building may put pool users at risk from the cold. If the pool has to be evacuated during an emergency in the winter time, provision must be made to protect pool users. Many pools now have supplies of heat-retaining 'space blankets'. These provide effective short term protection from the cold for evacuated pool users.

Diagnosis

The onset of body cooling may be almost unnoticed so awareness of the potential risk is essential. Early signs may include shivering, behavioural changes, slurred speech, lack of co-ordination and slowing of physical and mental activity.

Treatment

Alert the lifeguard team and summon assistance to move the casualty to a warm area. Prevent further heat loss by wrapping the casualty in a blanket, rug or sleeping bag, including cover for the head.

Re-warming should be passive with heat coming from the core of the body rather than the surface. Even in a warm environment, the casualty should be kept wrapped to insulate them from external heat. If re-warming occurs too quickly from the surface, there may be a potentially dangerous fall in blood pressure.

A warm, sweet drink can be offered if the casualty is fully conscious and able to swallow. This will have little effect on raising body temperature but may be comforting. Do not give alcohol.

Maintain close observation of the casualty's breathing and circulation. Obtain qualified medical aid as soon as possible or transfer the casualty to hospital.

It is important to ask the casualty about any illness such as diabetes or epilepsy as this information may be valuable to subsequent medical treatment.

BLEEDING, BURNS AND SCALDS

BLEEDING

Lifeguards are quite likely to encounter casualties who are bleeding. As well as the notes below, lifeguards should also read the notes on hygiene earlier in this chapter.

Blood loss reduces the amount of oxygen that can be carried to the organs and tissues of the body. Severe bleeding can lead to shock and ultimately death.

Bleeding can be external (for instance, from a cut) or internal (for instance, from rupture of tissue following a severe blow or a crush injury).

Bleeding may be from an artery (arterial bleeding), from a vein (venous bleeding) or from capillaries.

If an artery is severed, oxygenated blood, bright red and under pressure from the heart, will spurt from the wound in time with the heartbeat. A severed artery can rapidly drain the circulation, leading to shock and death.

If a vein is severed, blood that is dark red in colour may gush quite profusely although under less pressure than arterial blood.

Capillary bleeding occurs at the site of most wounds but is particularly associated with grazes. Bruising is a form of capillary bleeding in which capillaries are ruptured by a blow and bleed into tissues below the skin.

WHEN DEALING WITH BLEEDING, LIFEGUARDS SHOULD FOLLOW THE HYGIENE RECOMMENDATIONS SET OUT EARLIER IN THIS CHAPTER.

FIGURE 7-17
APPLYING A PAD AND
BANDAGE TO THE WOUND.

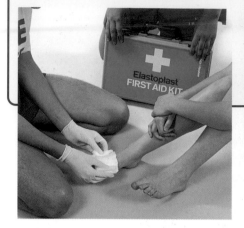

FIGURE 7-18
RAISING AND SUPPORTING
AN INJURED LIMB.

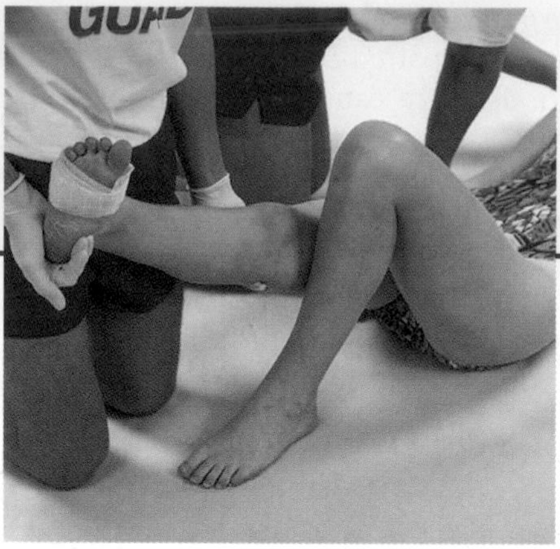

FIGURE 7-19
APPLYING PRESSURE ON
EITHER SIDE OF THE WOUND.

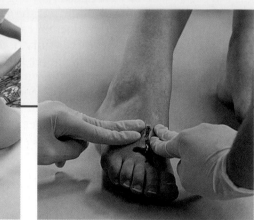

Diagnosis

External bleeding is usually obvious but a quick examination of the whole casualty, including any necessary removal of clothing, will ensure that no hidden bleeding is missed.

Internal bleeding is more difficult to diagnose. Signs of shock may be present and the casualty should be treated as described earlier in this chapter.

Treatment

When dealing with bleeding, lifeguards should wear protective gloves if possible.

If the bleeding is severe, alert the lifeguard team and summon medical aid as set out in the EAP.

Apply direct pressure to the wound using a clean pad or dressing (Fig. 7-17). If a dressing is not available, use the fingers or the palm of the hand. If the bleeding does not stop, do not remove the dressings but apply more on top of the first. If the wound is large, it may be more effective to press the edges together with your fingers.

Lay the casualty down in a comfortable position. Where possible raise the injured part of the body and support it (Fig. 7-18).

Treat the casualty for shock, make sure medical aid has been summoned or take the casualty to a doctor or hospital.

Scalp and head wounds may be associated with more serious injury to the skull as described earlier in this chapter. It is important to assess such casualties very carefully.

For minor bleeding, apply direct pressure to the wound, preferably using a dressing or pad of clean material. Do this gently but firmly. If there is an obvious foreign body in the wound, do not apply dressings over the foreign body but apply pressure to the edges of the wound (Fig. 7-19).

Lay the casualty down in a comfortable position and raise and support the injured part if possible. Even with minor wounds, further treatment may still be required to guard against infection.

Bleeding from the nose

Spontaneous nosebleeds are a fairly common occurrence for some people and are more of a nuisance than a danger. Bleeding may also result from a blow to the nose or violent sneezing and some casualties lose a lot of blood.

Treatment

Sit the casualty down with their head held forward. Ask them to breathe through their mouth and apply pressure to the soft tissue on both sides of the nose just below the bridge. This pressure can be applied by the casualty or the lifeguard (Fig. 7-20).

FIGURE 7-20
DEALING WITH A
NOSEBLEED.

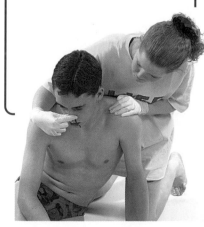

The pressure should be applied for up to ten minutes and then be released to allow circulation. Although pressure can then be reapplied for a further ten minutes, the treatment is usually effective within a few minutes. Ask the casualty not to speak, swallow, cough or sniff, as this may dislodge the newly formed blood clot.

If bleeding from the nose continues, medical aid should be summoned or the casualty transferred to hospital.

BURNS AND SCALDS

Lifeguards are unlikely to encounter burns and scalds on the pool side. However, such injuries may occur in other areas of the building such as the kitchen or plant room, so lifeguards may have to give first aid for burns from cooking, electric shock or chemicals.

Diagnosis

Burns are usually obvious. The casualty will be in pain and there may be blistering and swelling. In some cases, however, serious burns may cause little pain because the whole thickness of the skin, including the nerves, has been destroyed.

If a large area of the body has been burned, the loss of fluid and the pain can lead to shock.

If casualties are unconscious, look for scorching, skin damage or reddening if a burn is suspected.

FIGURE 7-21
TREATING A BURN ON THE ARM.

Treatment

Unless the burn or scald is minor, alert the lifeguard team and summon qualified medical aid.

The burned area should be immersed in cold running water if possible, and kept there for ten minutes to draw the heat out of the injured area. The water must be as cold as possible (Fig. 7-21).

If clothing has become stuck to the burned area, do not attempt to remove it as this may cause further damage.

Remove any rings, watches or jewellery carefully before the injured area starts to swell. Cover the burn with a clean sterile dressing held in place with a lightly applied bandage.

Never burst blisters as this will cause infection and lead to further fluid loss. Do not apply creams, oils or lotions to any affected part.

Treat the casualty for shock and ensure that medical aid is obtained.

In the case of chemical burns, qualified medical aid must be summoned immediately. Lifeguards must be familiar with relevant legislation and be aware of what chemicals are likely to be found on the premises, especially in the plant room.

ASTHMA, DIABETES AND EPILEPSY

ASTHMA

Asthma occurs when the muscles of the air passages go into spasm and narrow the airway. This, combined with the accumulation of mucus in the airway, causes shortness of breath and wheezing. People are usually quite well between attacks, which may come on suddenly and pass off again just as quickly. Asthma is less likely to occur while swimming, probably because the air above the water is moist.

People with asthma usually carry medication (often in the form of an inhaler) to open up the airway during an attack. Their medication should be easily accessible and they should bring it to the pool side.

In some cases, anxiety may bring on an attack. The sufferer should not swim if already wheezy, unless medication relieves their breathing difficulties.

FIGURE 7-22
MEDICATION CAN
RELIEVE AN ASTHMA
ATTACK.

If a pool user suffers an asthma attack, lifeguards should:

• reassure the casualty;

• assist them from the water;

• sit them down on a chair or seat, inclining their body slightly forward; and

• encourage the use of prescribed medication (Fig. 7-22).

If the attack is mild and rapidly relieved by medication, the casualty can return to the pool but lifeguards should maintain observation in case of a further attack. If the attack is severe or unrelieved by medication, or if the person becomes very distressed, lifeguards should summon qualified medical aid.

Further information may be obtained from the National Asthma Campaign.

DIABETES

Diabetes occurs when there is a disturbance in the body's ability to regulate blood sugar levels. This can result in:

• hyperglycaemia (too much blood sugar); or

• hypoglycaemia (too little blood sugar).

Both conditions can result in unconsciousness and eventually death.

As hyperglycaemia normally develops very gradually, lifeguards will rarely encounter casualties in this condition. Hypoglycaemia, however, can develop quickly in various ways.

Diagnosis of hypoglycaemia

The cause of hypoglycaemia is usually insufficient food or excess insulin in the body.

Signs include pallor of the skin, profuse sweating, rapid pulse and shallow breathing. Casualties may feel faint or become unconscious. The casualty's limbs may tremble, they may appear confused and occasionally become aggressive. In this condition, casualties can easily be mistaken for someone who is drunk.

Treatment

Conscious casualties should be given drinks sweetened with two or three table-spoons of sugar. If the casualty improves dramatically, the problem was an excess of insulin. If they do not improve, giving sugar will cause no harm.

Unconscious casualties should be placed in the recovery position, their breathing and circulation closely observed and qualified medical aid summoned immediately.

EPILEPSY

Epilepsy occurs when brain activity is suddenly disrupted and is marked by the tendency to recurrent seizures (sometimes referred to as 'fits'). Seizures can take many forms and the type of epilepsy is determined by whether all or only part of the brain is affected.

Generalised seizures (also referred to as 'major seizures') occur when a large part of the brain is involved.

Easily recognised generalised seizures include;

• clonic, in which the person becomes rigid, then falls to the ground making jerking movements;

• tonic, in which there is a general stiffening of muscles without rhythmical jerking and the person falls to the ground;

• atonic, in which there is a sudden collapse to the ground (also known as 'drop attacks'); and

• absences, in which there is a brief loss of consciousness without any other signs (absences can pass unnoticed as a person may appear to be daydreaming).

Partial seizures occur when the disturbance in brain activity involves a distinct area of the brain. There are two types of partial seizure:

- simple, in which consciousness is not impaired and the seizure is confined to either rhythmical twitching of a limb or sensations such as 'pins and needles' in a distinct part of the body; and

- complex or psychomotor, in which there is involuntary movement (twitching), plucking at clothing, lip-smacking, clouding of responsiveness and general confusion.

Complex partial seizures may be preceded by a strange feeling, unusual taste or smell, or other sensory disturbance. This phenomenon is called the 'aura'.

Swimming for people with epilepsy

Epilepsy may be associated with other disabilities referred to in Chapter Three. It is generally accepted that people with epilepsy should be allowed to swim provided:

- they have the approval of their doctor;

- they are accompanied by a strong swimmer, preferably one with some lifesaving training; and

- both are watched by a third person on the pool side who is aware of the situation (this includes observation by lifeguards).

A water temperature of 27°C (80°F) is recommended but between 25.5°C–29°C (78°F–84°F) is acceptable. Some public swimming pools fall outside this range.

Seizures in the water

In most cases, the person will be face down in the water during an attack. Very few people having a seizure thrash around in the water and so they may sink if not noticed.

After a non-convulsive seizure or absence, the person should be helped out of the water quietly and calmly.

During a convulsive seizure, the person should be supported to ensure their face is clear of the water. Care must be taken to ensure their head does not hit the lifeguard or the pool side. If possible, the person suffering the seizure should be supported in shallow water until the seizure is over and then assisted from the pool (Fig. 7-23).

Lifeguards should monitor breathing and circulation and be prepared to start cardio pulmonary resuscitation if needed.

Medical attention should be obtained for anyone who has a seizure in the water because if water has been inhaled there is a danger of secondary drowning.

Seizures on land

During a non-convulsive seizure or an absence the person may not require any attention other than observation and understanding.

During a convulsive seizure, the person should not be restrained and should only be moved if there is a danger of injury or falling into the water (Fig. 7-24). Objects which could cause injury should be removed.

Place the person in the recovery position as soon as possible to prevent inhalation of saliva or vomit.

Once the attack is over, the person should be allowed to rest quietly until they are fully recovered.

Summon qualified medical aid if there is any injury, if the attack lasts for more than five minutes, if the attack is repeated without consciousness being regained or if the seizure is unusual for that person.

Further information may be obtained from the British Epilepsy Association.

FIGURE 7-23
DEALING WITH A MINOR EPILEPTIC SEIZURE IN THE WATER.

FIGURE 7-24
SUPPORTING A CASUALTY WITH AN EPILEPTIC SEIZURE.

FRACTURES AND INJURIES TO MUSCLES AND LIGAMENTS

FRACTURES

Although pool users often slip on wet pool floors, the number of serious injuries is quite small. Treatment is usually restricted to dealing with bruising.

Fractures are uncommon but in leisure centres with sports facilities, gymnasiums and playing fields, lifeguards may have to deal with this type of injury.

Fractures take several forms. In an open fracture, a wound may lead down to a fracture or fractured ends of bone may protrude through the skin. In a closed fracture, the skin is not broken.

Complications can be associated with either open or closed fractures when there is injury to major blood vessels, brain, lungs, nerves, liver, joints and other parts of the body.

Spinal injuries, including fractures, are dealt with in Chapter Eight.

Diagnosis

Cracking sounds may be heard at the time of injury. Severe pain at the site of the injury is common but not always present. Movement of the injured area is restricted and painful. Swelling and deformity can often be seen (Fig. 7-25).

A limb may be bent at an unusual angle so lifeguards should compare one side of the body with the other.

Treatment

In the case of suspected fracture of any bones in the neck or spine, refer to Chapter Eight. In the case of a suspected fractured skull, summon qualified medical aid immediately (see earlier in this chapter).

Where possible, the casualty should be kept in the position in which they are found. If they have to be removed from the pool, alert the lifeguard team and exercise great care.

Cover any external wound with a clean, dry dressing. This may involve the use of a pad or similar device if the broken bone is protruding, arranged in such a way that it surrounds and protects the wound.

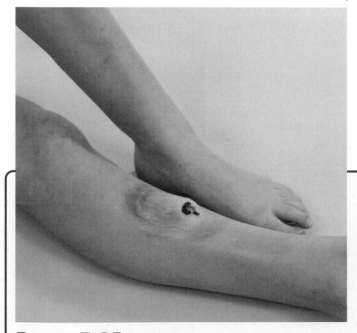

FIGURE 7-25
A TYPICAL OPEN FRACTURE.

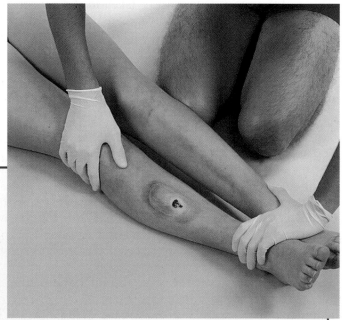

FIGURE 7-26
SUPPORTING THE INJURED LIMB.

Do not move any injured part of the body unless necessary. Support upper limbs by hand or with a sling and lower limbs with pads of blankets, clothing and so on, or by gently strapping one leg to the other with pads between the two (Fig. 7-26).

Arrange for the casualty to be transferred to hospital as soon as possible. Full use should be made of equipment such as stretchers, ambulance chairs and spine boards as appropriate.

DISLOCATION

Dislocation usually affects the shoulder and is very painful.

Casualties will be reluctant to try to move the affected joint because of the pain. If they are in the water, lifeguards should be very careful in assisting them onto the pool side.

The casualty should be allowed to find the most comfortable position for themselves and support for that position can then be provided by a sling. Lifeguards should not attempt to relocate the joint or do anything that might aggravate the injury but should seek qualified medical aid.

SPRAINS, STRAINS AND CRAMP

These types of injury are often classified as 'soft tissue injuries' because they affect the ligaments and the muscles.

Sprains

Sprains occur at joints where ligaments have been subject to a wrenching or tearing force. They are very painful and characterised by immobility of the joint, swelling, bruising and discoloration. The swelling will occur soon after the injury. Discoloration and bruising may show some time later.

Treatment for sprains

Make sure the casualty is comfortable and support the limb. If the injury is recent, apply a cold compress or ice bag. Protect with plenty of padding secured with bandages. Elevate the limb and transfer the casualty to hospital.

Strains

Strains occur if muscles become overstretched. A strain is usually unexpected and causes intense pain at the site of the injury. If it occurs in a limb, the muscles may swell and produce severe cramp.

Treatment for strains

Elevate the injured limb if possible. If the injury is recent, apply a cold compress or ice bag. Apply compression with a crepe bandage soaked in water and wrung out.

Cramp

Cramp is a sudden, involuntary and painful contraction of a muscle. Cramp is dangerous if it occurs while the casualty is in the water because it may impair swimming ability. Cramp can be caused by very cold conditions, sudden or unusual exercise, a blow or injury to the muscle, or by excessive loss of salt from severe sweating.

The casualty will feel pain in a muscle, often in the calf or the trunk. The affected muscle feels hard and tight and the casualty is unable to relax it.

Treatment for cramp

Stretch the muscle by carefully and gently straightening the affected area. If the calf muscle is affected, straighten the knee and gently push the casualty's toes towards the knee. If the abdominal muscles are affected, encourage the casualty to stand straight and arch the back slightly.

Massage the affected area very gently to help the muscle to relax. The muscle must not be rubbed violently. Advise the casualty to rest before further activity.

EYE AND DENTAL INJURIES, INSECT STINGS

EYES

Particles of grit and dust or loose eyelashes are the most common foreign objects found in the eyes. They stick to the inner surface of the eyelid (most often the upper one) causing discomfort and inflammation. In most cases they can be removed easily. However, never attempt to remove a foreign body if it is on the coloured part of the eye or embedded in the eyeball. Summon medical aid immediately.

The eye will be painful or itch, vision may be impaired and the eye will water. Often the area around the eye will be red and painful.

Any eye injury is potentially serious and can result in damage, infection or blindness.

Treatment

Advise the casualty not to rub the eye. Sit the casualty down facing the light. Stand behind the casualty, and gently separate the eyelids with your finger and thumb. Examine every part of the eye. If the foreign body can be seen, wash it out with a sterile solution or tap water using an eye glass or eye irrigation unit.

If this is unsuccessful, carefully apply an eye pad and bandage the affected eye and seek qualified medical aid.

If the eyes have been exposed to direct glare from the sun, casualties may feel pain or discomfort and the eyes may feel 'gritty', water and redden. The eyes should be bathed in clean, cold water, and a light dressing applied. Medical aid should be sought if the irritation is severe.

Extra care will be needed if the casualty is wearing contact lenses.

DENTAL INJURIES

If a casualty falls or is struck in the mouth, there will be bleeding and the teeth may be damaged.

Treatment

If a tooth is broken or chipped, lifeguards should retrieve any broken parts if possible. The casualty should rinse their mouth with warm water and apply a cold pack on the outside of the cheek and seek attention from a dentist.

If a tooth is knocked right out, it should be retrieved and put it in a container with milk. The casualty should seek attention from a dentist, taking the tooth to the consultation.

If the tooth socket is bleeding, ensure the casualty places a sterile pad of gauze over the socket and applies a steady biting pressure on the pad.

INSECT STINGS AND BITES

Stings from insects such as bees, wasps and hornets are usually more painful and alarming than they are dangerous.

Some people are allergic to the poison and multiple stings from a swarm of insects can have a dangerous cumulative effect. In either case, there is a danger of anaphylatic shock.

Stings in the mouth and throat may cause swelling leading to suffocation.

Treatment

Remove the sting, if it is still there, being careful not to squeeze any poison sac. Apply a cold compress to relieve pain and swelling. Advise the casualty to seek medical aid if the pain or swelling persists.

For stings in the mouth, the casualty should suck ice for immediate relief. Qualified medical aid should be summoned or the casualty transferred to hospital.

TEST YOURSELF

1. What are the aims of first aid?

2. Describe some of the things to look for during secondary assessment.

3. What hygiene measures should be considered when dealing with blood?

4. What does diagnosis mean?

5. Why is it important to keep a record of a casualty's progress?

6. Describe how to place an unconscious casualty in the recovery position.

7. What provisions should be made to ensure aftercare?

8. When would you use a sling?

9. What serious consequences might follow a head injury?

10. What can lead to loss of consciousness?

11. Describe some signs that may precede fainting.

12. What is the most common cause of a heart attack?

13. How do you tell the difference between a choking casualty and one suffering a heart attack?

14. Describe techniques to relieve a choking casualty.

15. Which technique for relieving choking should not be used on babies and young children?

16. What is shock and what are its potential consequences?

17. What is analphylatic shock?

18. Describe the precautions when giving rescue breathing to a casualty who has suffered poisoning from gas or toxic fumes.

19. What is the priority when rescuing someone who has received an electric shock?

20. What is hypothermia and how should it be treated?

21. What is the difference between venous and arterial bleeding?

22. How would you treat severe bleeding?

23. What is the treatment for a burn or scald?

24. Describe the signs and symptoms of hypoglycaemia and how to treat it.

25. Describe the most common forms of seizure seen in epilepsy.

26. How would you manage an epileptic seizure?

27. What is a fracture and how would you treat it?

28. What is the difference between a strain and a sprain?

29. How would you treat cramp?

8

Spinal Cord Injury Management

THIS CHAPTER COVERS:

- THE IMPORTANCE OF TEAMWORK AND TRAINING IN MANAGING SPINAL INJURIES.

- THE ANATOMY OF THE SPINE; VERTEBRAE; PERIPHERAL AND AUTONOMIC NERVES.

- TYPES AND CAUSES OF SPINAL INJURIES; SIGNS AND SYMPTOMS; THE IMPORTANCE OF STABILISING THE HEAD AND SPINE.

- INCIDENT MANAGEMENT; THE PRIORITY TO SAVE LIFE; EMERGENCY ACTION; THE VICE GRIP, BEAR HUG AND LOG ROLL.

- RECOVERY WITH AND WITHOUT A SPINE BOARD; LIFTING CASUALTIES FROM THE WATER; SAFETY DURING SPINAL RESCUES.

FIGURE 8-1 SLIDES POSE A POTENTIAL RISK OF SPINAL INJURIES.

FIGURE 8-2 THE LIFEGUARD TEAM MANAGING A SPINAL INJURY.

Spinal Cord Injury Management

HE EFFECTS of spinal cord injury can be catastrophic. The result may be paralysis of a single limb (called monoplegia), paralysis of one side of the body (hemiplegia), paralysis of the lower limbs (paraplegia) or paralysis of all four limbs (tetraplegia or quadraplegia).

The way lifeguards deal with a suspected spinal cord injury is crucial to the eventual outcome. Only half of all spinal injuries lead to irreparable damage at the moment the accident occurs. In the other half, the damage caused at the time of injury leaves the potential for recovery provided no further damage occurs. How the casualty is handled determines whether further damage is done.

It is vital that lifeguards are aware of the risk of aggravating suspected spinal cord injury by taking inappropriate action. Actions which do not take account of this risk could result in the casualty becoming permanently paralysed. The arrangements for dealing with suspected spinal injuries must be set out in the pool's Emergency Action Plan (EAP).

Spinal injuries in swimming pools are traditionally associated with diving. Lifeguards and pool operators are referred to *It's Your Knock,* a leaflet produced by the Amateur Swimming Association which covers diving safety. Further guidance can be found in the ISRM publication *Diving into Swimming Pools.* The growing popularity of pool features such as slides, chutes, and flumes has also increased the potential risk of spinal injuries (Fig. 8-1).

Proper handling of a casualty with a suspected spinal injury requires at least four trained people. At least two of them must be trained to NPLQ level (with endorsement for the use of the spine board). The lifeguards must be supported by at least two other team members who are trained in the use of the spine board. Many pools may not have more than two lifeguards on duty at any one time, so back up and support will be from other trained members of staff such as receptionists, cleaners or caterers depending on their availability and level of training.

Because teamwork and training are essential to the safe management of spinal injuries, pool operators should provide regular training sessions to build an efficient team (Fig. 8-2).

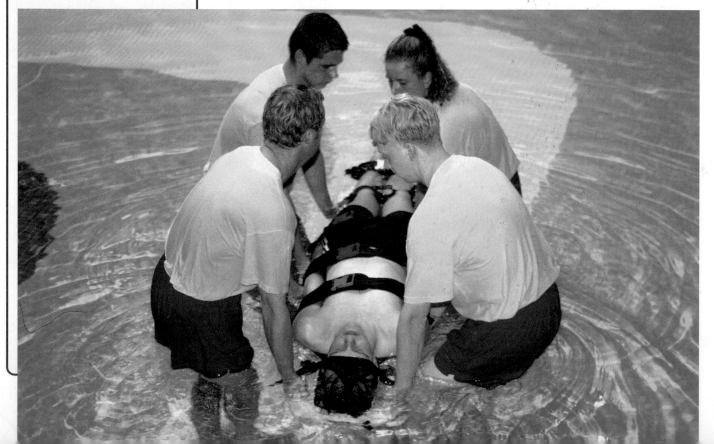

As part of lifeguards' in-service training, it is important that all aspects of rescuing spinal injury casualties, including recovery with a spine board, are practised. This may include liaison with the emergency services to ensure that ambulance staff are aware of the manner in which the rescue will take place and the way that the board will be used.

ANATOMY OF THE SPINE

Lifeguards need a basic understanding of the anatomy of the spine to help them identify possible injuries and deal with them appropriately.

The spine supports the skull and gives attachment to the ribs. It is made up of 33 irregular bones called vertebrae (the singular is a vertebra) arranged in a flexible column. The vertebrae have discs of cartilage between them which allow limited movement, prevent friction and act as shock absorbers (Fig. 8-3).

The vertebrae are divided into five groups:

- seven cervical vertebrae in the neck;
- twelve thoracic vertebrae to which the ribs attach;
- five lumbar vertebrae in the lower back;
- five sacral vertebrae, fused to form the sacrum; and
- four coccygeal vertebrae, fused to form the coccyx.

The spinal cord runs through a canal in the centre of the spinal column and is made of nervous tissue extending from the brain stem to the second lumbar vertebra. The functions of the spinal cord are to link the brain to the nerves in the limbs and outer parts of the trunk, and to provide links to the centre of reflex action. The spinal cord therefore affects every nerve in the body other than the cranial nerves.

Nerves in pairs run off the spinal cord throughout its length, the large ones to the limbs leaving in the cervical and lumbar regions. Nerves can be classified into two categories — the peripheral nerves and the autonomic nerves.

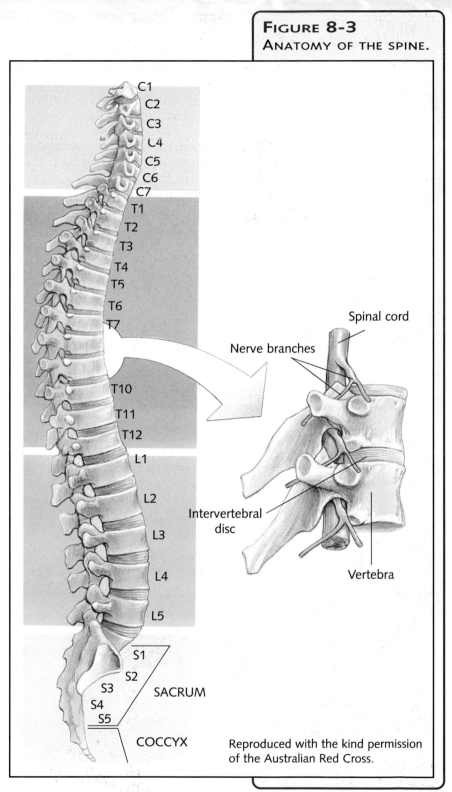

FIGURE 8-3
ANATOMY OF THE SPINE.

C1
C2
C3
C4
C5
C6
C7
T1
T2
T3
T4
T5
T6
T7
T10
T11
T12
L1
L2
L3
L4
L5
S1
S2
S3
S4
S5
SACRUM
COCCYX

Spinal cord
Nerve branches
Intervertebral disc
Vertebra

Reproduced with the kind permission of the Australian Red Cross.

PERIPHERAL NERVES

There are two types of peripheral nerve, sensory and motor. Sensory nerves carry information about the external world (pain, temperature, touch, position) from the skin, joints and muscles to the spinal cord and thus the brain.

Motor nerves carry signals from the brain to activate muscles and produce physical movement.

Reflexes combine sensory and motor signals, through the spinal cord, to allow rapid response to potential damage. They act without voluntary (conscious) control by the brain. An example is moving a hand away from a painful stimulus, such as heat, before the brain signals 'pain'.

AUTONOMIC NERVES

The autonomic nervous system controls the internal organs of the body and the blood vessels. It is so called because the functioning of the internal organs normally takes place without conscious effort or awareness. Autonomic nerves control involuntary muscles such as the heart, breathing and the pupils of the eye.

The autonomic nervous system comprises two sets of nerves, the sympathetic and the parasympathetic. Sympathetic nerves have a stimulating and quickening effect on the heart, circulatory and respiratory systems, but a checking effect on digestion. Parasympathetic nerves have the opposite effect, stimulating the digestion, slowing the heart and reducing the circulation and respiration.

SPINAL INJURIES

Spinal injury may result from a fall, especially from a height onto a hard surface such as the pool side, by a blow to the neck or head, or by striking the bottom of the pool after diving into water which is too shallow (usually defined as under 1.5 metres deep).

As we have seen, damage to the spinal cord may result in partial or complete paralysis (See Fig. 6-4, page 106). To avoid aggravating the damage, careful handling, lifting and moving are essential when dealing with spinal injuries. So it is important that lifeguards look for any sign or symptom of spinal injury after an accident.

Symptoms of damage to the spinal cord and nerves include:

- lack of movement in one or more limbs;
- numbness or tingling in the limbs; and
- disorientation or bewilderment.

Other signs and symptoms include:

- bruising of the head;
- bruising or swelling of the neck;
- pain in the neck; and
- pain in the back.

See the diagram at right.

TYPES OF INJURY

Spinal injuries can involve either the vertebrae or the discs of cartilage (ligaments) or both (Fig. 8-4).

Vertebral fracture

This term means that one or more of the individual bones in the spine is broken. A fracture of a vertebra (or vertebrae) can lead to bone pushing into the canal in which the spinal cord runs. When the canal is compressed, the spinal cord is crushed.

FIGURE 8-4
RECOGNITION OF SPINAL INJURY

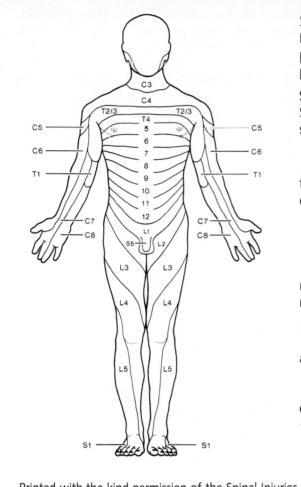

Signs of injury to the spinal cord
Damage to the spinal cord may result in either permanent or temporary paralysis, which may be partial or complete.

Signs and symptoms
Signs and symptoms include pain caused by the impact, such as:

- bruising of the head and/or neck;
- pain in the neck.

the results of incorrect or inappropriate transmission of nerve signals, such as:

- lack of movement of one or more limbs;
- disorientation or bewilderment;
- numbness or tingling in the limbs.

The serious consequences of damage to the central nervous system mean that careful handling, lifting and moving are essential when dealing with spinal injuries.

This body outline indicates the areas of the body affected by damage to groups of vertebrae.

C 1–7   CERVICAL
T 1–12 THORACIC
L 1–5   LUMBAR

Printed with the kind permission of the Spinal Injuries Association.

Vertebral dislocation
As we have seen, the spine is a column of bones held together by discs of cartilage or ligaments. If these ligaments are torn, one bone can move forwards or backwards in relation to the other. Although the canal in each individual vertebra remains the correct size, the shift of position reduces the size of the canal between the vertebrae so the spinal cord is crushed. In extreme cases, the ligaments can be so badly damaged that only spasm of the muscles holds the spine together.

   If the ligaments at the back of the vertebrae are torn, the vertebra above usually slides forwards over the vertebra below. If the ligaments at the front are torn, the upper vertebra usually slides backwards over the vertebra below. In either case, the canal will be compromised and the spinal cord crushed.

Flexion injuries
When the head is forced forwards, the ligaments are stretched and torn at the back. This is called a flexion injury.

Extension injuries
If the head is forced backwards, the ligaments at the front are torn and the bones can slide backwards. This is called an extension injury. If the head is forced back further, the damage will be increased.

STABILISING THE HEAD

Moving the head in the same direction as the original injury can cause further damage to the spinal cord. To prevent aggravating the injury, the casualty's head must be maintained in a neutral position. It must not be allowed to bend forwards, backwards, sideways, or be twisted.

Only if the casualty's head remains in a neutral position will the canal be likely to retain the maximum possible size thus minimising spinal cord compression. The neutral position helps prevent vertebra sliding either forwards or backwards and reduces the chance of fractured fragments of a vertebra damaging the spinal cord.

Stabilising the entire spine

One of the problems of suspected spinal injuries is that lifeguards can't be certain which part of the spine has been damaged. Although the cervical spine should be dealt with first, the rest of the spine should be stabilised as soon as possible. In deep water, the body's natural buoyancy may help to provide stability. But once the casualty has reached a point of support, it is important that additional support is given to the spine. When casualties with suspected spinal injuries are removed from the water, it is vital they are maintained in a horizontal position. Conventional lifts, most of which result in vertical movement out of the water, can have disastrous consequences.

For instance, attempting to lift a casualty by the armpits will place great strain on the spinal column as the weight of the lower body and legs becomes unsupported by the water. The unstabilised head is liable to move causing further injury. And lifting the casualty vertically can lead to a sudden drop in blood pressure which can result in cardiac arrest.

Summary

In summary, the spine is made up of individual vertebrae and houses the spinal cord. The spinal cord is the centre of the nervous system and damage to it can result in paralysis. Injury can occur anywhere along the length of the spine.

Spinal damage can take the form of flexion injuries, compression injuries or extension injuries. It may be impossible for lifeguards to tell which sort of injury has occurred.

The first priority in successfully managing a spinal injury is to stabilise the casualty's head.

The second priority is to maintain the casualty in a horizontal position.

INCIDENT MANAGEMENT

A LIFEGUARD'S FIRST PRIORITY MUST BE TO SAVE LIFE

Sometimes there may be a conflict between the need to stabilise casualties with suspected spinal injuries and the need to save their life. For instance, a casualty may fall from a diving platform, hitting the edge of the pool before falling face down into the water. The casualty must obviously be turned face-up as soon as possible and, if not breathing, be given rescue breathing. Opening the airway to allow the casualty to breathe may mean moving the head thus aggravating a suspected spinal injury.

Action to resuscitate a casualty with a suspected spinal injury may result in paralysis. Failure to attempt resuscitation will result in death. Lifeguards must base their decision on the priority of saving life.

EMERGENCY ACTION

Emergency action must be in accordance with the pool's EAP and should be based on teamwork. The overriding considerations are:

- ensuring a clear airway;
- stabilising the head;
- maintaining the casualty in a horizontal position; and
- immobilising the spine.

In the notes below, we assume that the casualty is in the water. Both the 'vice grip' and the 'bear hug' described below are intended to prevent forward, backward, lateral or twisting movement of the head and neck.

If the casualty is in deep water, they should be 'trawled' to a point where the lifeguard can stand comfortably.

In Foundation Module training and in the notes below, a team is assumed to consist of at least four trained people, two of whom must be qualified lifeguards.

If a spine board is used to remove a casualty from the water, stabilising the casualty's head and neck is still the priority (Fig. 8-5).

THE VICE GRIP (CASUALTY FACE DOWN)

The lifeguard should approach the casualty from one side to secure their head, neck and torso in the vice grip.

Reach under the casualty, taking care to go round their near arm rather than under it. Place your forearm along the line of the casualty's sternum (breastbone), supporting their chin securely with your thumb and fingers either side of the jaw.

Place your other forearm in the corresponding position along the casualty's spine. Your fingers should be outstretched on the back of the head, clamping it securely from behind. Aim to make your arm actions simultaneous (Fig. 8-6 A).

Always place the elbows in position first, to ensure a secure position for your hands which have to stabilise the casualty's neck.

Keep your fingers, hands, wrists and elbows rigid; your elbows and forearms should be gently but firmly pressed together like a vice holding an object between its jaws.

Secured in the vice grip, the casualty can be turned face up. To do so, the lifeguard must slide beneath the casualty under the water. Maintaining the vice grip to prevent movement of the head or spine, the casualty can be slowly rolled face up on to the surface of the water (Fig. 8-6 B).

If the water is deeper than standing depth, the lifeguard will need to kick hard to ensure that the casualty is not pulled below the surface.

FIGURE 8-5
CPR FOR A SPINAL CASUALTY.

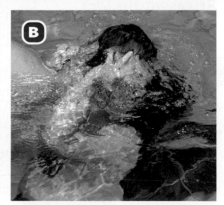

FIGURE 8-6
A VICE GRIP WITH BOTH ARMS.
B VICE GRIP, TURNING THE CASUALTY.

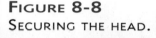

FIGURE 8-7
APPLYING THE VICE GRIP.

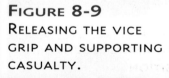

FIGURE 8-8
SECURING THE HEAD.

FIGURE 8-9
RELEASING THE VICE
GRIP AND SUPPORTING
CASUALTY.

THE VICE GRIP (CASUALTY FACE UP)

Occasionally, a casualty may be face up in the water. The lifeguard should approach the casualty from one side to secure their head, neck and torso in the vice grip as above. This time, however, the lower arm should be placed into position first. It is important to ensure that the grip is secured in such a way that there is no movement of the head or neck in relation to the torso (Fig. 8-7).

ASSISTANCE TO STABILISE CASUALTIES

Maintaining the vice grip is physically very demanding and assistance is needed as soon as possible. Additional support should be given by at least two trained people, at least one of whom must be a qualified lifeguard.

The rescuing lifeguard should direct the second lifeguard to stand at the casualty's head and place one hand gently but firmly on each side of the head, so that the forefinger and thumb are above and below the casualty's ears (Fig. 8-8).

Without releasing the vice grip, the rescuing lifeguard should instruct another trained person to gently support the base of the spine and buttocks with his forearms.

The rescuing lifeguard can then remove the upper hand from the sternum and place the forearm, with hand palm down, under the middle of the casualty's back. The rescuing lifeguard's other hand can be removed from its position down the line of the spine and placed under the casualty's shoulders (Fig. 8-9).

It is essential that stabilisation is maintained throughout the changing of hand positions.

Once a trained person is available they should provide additional support to the lower limbs by placing their forearms under the back of the ankles and calves.

Once stabilised in this position, the casualty is ready to be removed from the water. This should be done as quickly as possible to prevent the onset of hypothermia and to allow cardio pulmonary resuscitation if it is necessary.

THE BEAR HUG (CASUALTY FACE DOWN)

It is extremely difficult (though not impossible) for a lifeguard to apply the vice grip and turn the casualty in shallow water.

If the water is less than about 0.7 metres (2 ft 6 ins), the bear hug technique should be used to turn and secure the casualty.

This technique relies on the support of the lifeguard team. It is essential that at least two team members are in the water before one lifeguard uses this method to secure and turn a face down casualty.

The rescuing lifeguard should approach the casualty from one side, lean over the casualty and slide the arms under the casualty's armpits. The hands are then stretched upwards to grasp the casualty's head on each side. The fingers should be outstretched and the thumb and forefinger placed above and below the casualty's ears (Fig. 8-10 A).

The casualty's head and neck are stabilised by locking the fingers, wrists, forearms and elbows. Gentle pressure should be applied to either side of the casualty's head and torso.

The casualty can then be turned face up by the lifeguard dropping one shoulder and using the opposite leg to push off, rolling under the casualty (Fig. 8-10 B). The lifeguard may be lying on the pool bottom with the casualty on top, the casualty's head and neck secured by the bear hug grip.

The lifeguard will now be submerged under the casualty. It is vital that other team members immediately provide support to the casualty's head and upper torso.

Once the casualty is lying face up, the second lifeguard should place his hands on top of the first lifeguard's hands either side of the casualty's head (Fig. 8-10 C). At the same time, another lifeguard or trained person should gently support the casualty's lower back and buttocks. This is primarily a sliding action without losing hold of the casualty.

When the first lifeguard sees that the additional support for the casualty's head is in place and can feel that the lower back and buttocks are supported, he can begin to relax the bear hug and gently slide his hands out from underneath the hands of the second lifeguard. He can then slide slowly out, sideways, from under the casualty (Fig. 8-10 D).

Should the trained person not arrive at the scene until the rescue is underway, the rescuing lifeguard may need to move out from under the casualty. This should not be attempted before the casualty's head has been supported. Once out from under the casualty, the rescuing lifeguard should position himself to maintain support to the back and buttocks while awaiting the arrival of a third team member.

Lifeguards must decide whether the water is too shallow for either the vice grip or the bear hug to be used. If the water is too shallow it may be necessary to use the log roll.

LOG ROLL

If casualties vomit, whether or not they are on a spine board, they should be turned onto their side. Log rolling is the method of turning a casualty onto one side by moving the head, neck, torso and hips as one, keeping them in line (Fig. 8-11).

Depending on the size of the casualty, as many as six team members may be needed. It is essential that lifeguards are trained in undertaking this manoeuvre.

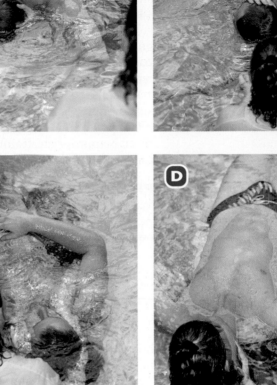

FIGURE 8-10
A RESCUING LIFEGUARD IN POSITION.
B TURNING THE CASUALTY.
C LIFEGUARD UNDER CASUALTY.
D LIFEGUARD SURFACES HOLDING CASUALTY.

FIGURE 8-11
LOG ROLL - AN ADDITIONAL LIFEGUARD MAY BE NEEDED IN FRONT OF THE CASUALTY.

RECOVERY WITH A SPINE BOARD

Removing casualties from the water using a spine board minimises the risk of aggravating suspected spinal injuries. It reduces unnecessary movement of the casualty during this critical manoeuvre.

The spine board used and recommended by RLSS UK is the Ferno Aquaboard.

This board ensures that the casualty's whole body is supported and it is sufficiently rigid not to flex as the casualty is lifted from the water.

Training and assessment for using the Ferno Aquaboard should be in accordance with health and safety legislation and workplace equipment regulations. Reference should also be made to Ferno's literature.

If other spine boards are used operationally and for in-service training, pool operators should ensure appropriate training is provided. They should also ensure lifeguards and support staff have access to the manufacturers' instructions and handbooks. Under workplace equipment regulations, these documents must be retained on site and be available to employees.

The spine board should be stored, vertically on its wall bracket, either on the pool side or immediately adjacent to it allowing immediate access.

The pool's EAP will govern the use of spine boards and the lifeguard should receive appropriate training during the Professional (Site Specific) Module of the NPLQ.

PREPARING FOR RECOVERY

With the casualty supported in the water by at least two lifeguards and one trained person, another trained person should prepare the board for use. The EAP will set out the procedure for preparing the board while other team members stabilise the casualty.

The board should be prepared on the pool side or in the water. The straps and head restraint should be loosened for use (Fig. 8-12). As the board is placed in the water, the straps nearest to the casualty should be eased under the board to prevent them becoming tangled.

The board should be positioned alongside the casualty, the head markings on the board aligned with the casualty's head (Fig. 8-13 A). The board should then be lifted so that the long side nearest the casualty is in the water and the surface of the board is vertical. In other words, the board is at right angles to the water, the top facing the casualty. From this position, the board can be pushed down into the water. The board is designed so that as it submerges it slides under the casualty. The board should then be controlled so that it floats gently up under the casualty.

With the casualty still supported by the team, the board can be correctly positioned relative to the casualty. The team member supporting the lower limbs can then gently slide the hands out, move to the foot end of the board and take hold of it (Fig. 8-13 B).

Similarly, the person supporting the shoulders and upper back can slide the hands out and move to support the head end of the board. At this stage, the team member supporting the casualty's head must maintain that support.

If three people are supporting the casualty's body and legs, it is recommended that the first moves to the foot of the board and the other two move to each side of the board at the shoulder position.

The person who positioned the board should now secure the casualty. The 'green' chest strap should be secured first and gently tightened (Fig. 8-13 C). This effectively secures the casualty onto the board. Following this, the head restraint should be positioned over the forehead and tightened by gently pulling the straps (Fig. 8-13 D).

Sometimes the build of the casualty means that to keep the head in line with their torso, it may be better to dip the foot end of the board down so that the other end rises to meet the casualty's head, rather than to lower the head onto the board.

As the head restraint is placed over the forehead, the person supporting the head should release the hold one hand at a time to allow the restraint to be correctly positioned. The head must be kept steady throughout this action (Fig. 8-13 E).

FIGURE 8-12
UNCLIP THE STRAPS WHILE ENTERING WATER.

FIGURE 8-13
RECOVERY WITH A SPINE BOARD

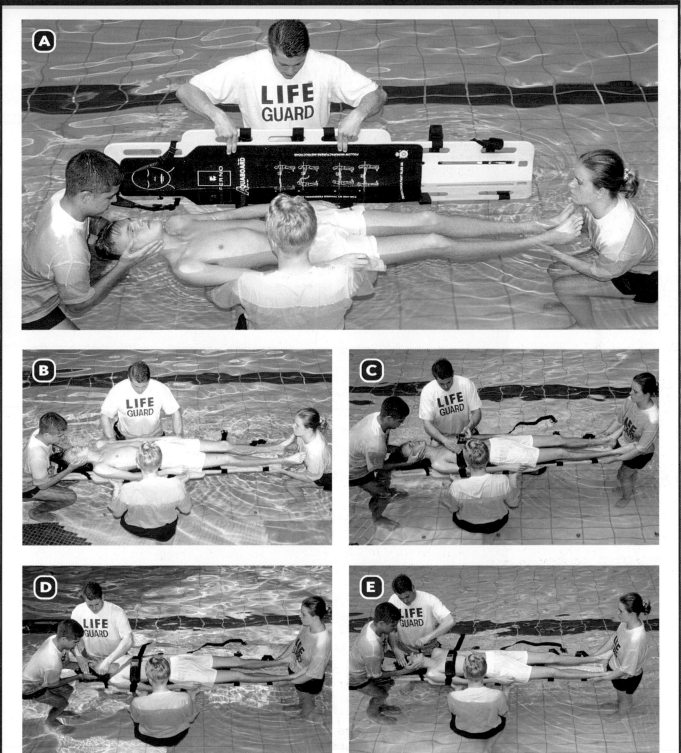

A PLACE THE SPINE BOARD ALONGSIDE CASUALTY. **B** REMOVE THE HANDS AFTER CASUALTY IS ON BOARD. **C** SECURING THE FIRST 'GREEN' STRAP. **D** POSITIONING THE HEAD RESTRAINT STRAP. **E** TAKE CARE TO KEEP THE HEAD STEADY.

FIGURE 8-14
SECURE THE REMAINING
STRAPS IN SEQUENCE.

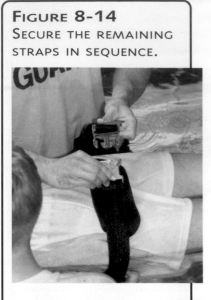

Once the head restraint is in place and correctly adjusted, the other coloured buckles can be secured and the straps tightened in the same order in which they were fastened (Fig. 8-14). The casualty is now ready to be removed from the water by the team.

REMOVING THE CASUALTY FROM THE WATER

The casualty must be removed from the water in a horizontal position. One team member should be on the pool side ready to receive the board as it comes out of the water. Two team members should support the head end of the board as this is the heavier end. The fourth team member should support the foot of the board. The team leader should be responsible for co-ordinating the manoeuvre and giving instructions (Fig. 8-15).

The recovery sequence is:

- place the head end of the board at right angles to the edge of the pool;
- on a count of 'three', lift the board and place the head end on the pool side;
- keep the board level; and
- gently slide the board fully onto the pool side (Fig. 8-16).

FIGURE 8-15
MOVING TO THE
POOL SIDE.

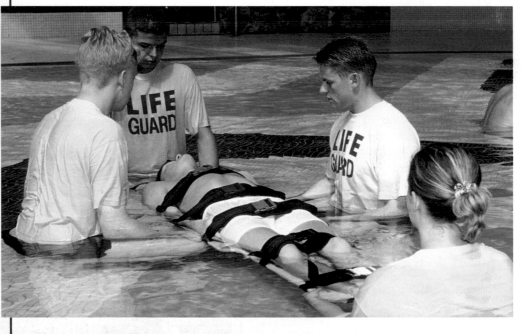

FIGURE 8-16
GENTLY SLIDING THE
BOARD ONTO THE
POOL SIDE.

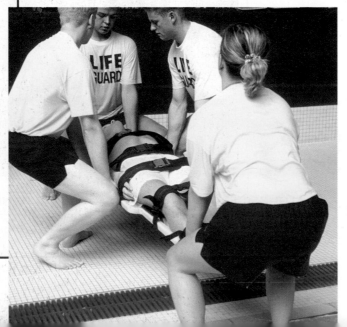

Once the board is on the pool side, it should be moved away from the water and resuscitation started if necessary (Fig. 8-17).

Lifeguards should remember that the casualty will feel extremely vulnerable while strapped on the board. The casualty will also require aftercare and treatment for shock.

If resuscitation is required, an open airway may be achieved by a combination of chin lift and carefully controlled head tilt. To minimise movement, these actions should be undertaken by two lifeguards (Fig. 8-18).

Although we have looked at rescues and recoveries with a team of four trained people, in many cases more team members may be available. This situation will be covered by the EAP at the specific pool and covered by in-service training.

RECOVERY WITHOUT A SPINE BOARD

In some circumstances, casualties with suspected spinal injuries may need to be removed from the water without a spine board.

Unless the casualty is very small, this needs at least two lifeguards and two trained people in the water with a further trained person on the pool side.

First, the casualty needs to be stabilised and supported in water no more than waist deep, as described above. The casualty should be horizontal, face up and parallel to the edge of the pool (Fig. 8-19). The positions of the five team members are:

- **Lifeguard A** should hold the casualty's head and stabilise it;
- **Lifeguard B** should be at the casualty's shoulders, supporting the upper part of the back;
- **Trained person C** should be at the casualty's hips, supporting the buttocks and lower spine;
- **Trained person D** should be at the casualty's legs, supporting them; and
- **Trained person E** should be on the pool side (Fig. 8-20).

Lifeguard B (the one supporting the upper part of the casualty's back) should control the recovery of the casualty throughout the manoeuvre.

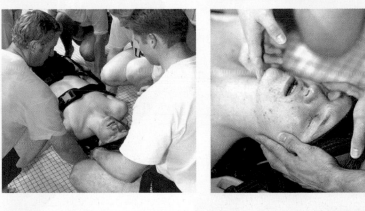

FIGURE 8-17 THE BOARD ON THE POOL SIDE.

FIGURE 8-18 RESCUE BREATHING CAN BE GIVEN IF NEEDED.

FIGURE 8-19 PREPARING TO HORIZONTAL LIFT.

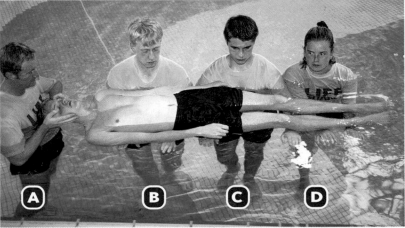

FIGURE 8-20 POSITION OF LIFEGUARDS BEFORE THE LIFT.

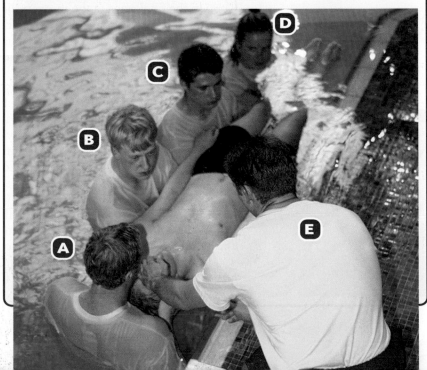

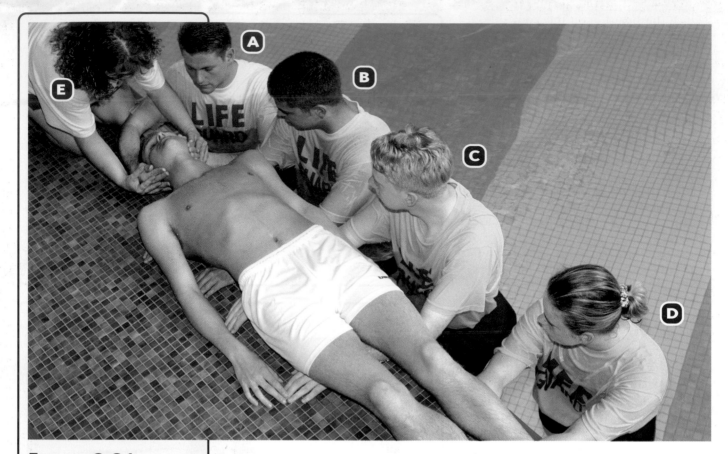

FIGURE 8-21
THE HORIZONTAL LIFT.

FIGURE 8-22
LIFEGUARDS REMOVING ARMS FROM UNDER THE CASUALTY.

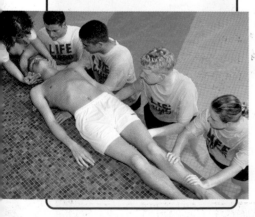

It is very important that the casualty stays horizontal throughout the lift. Lifeguard B should ensure that trained people C and D are adequately supporting the casualty on their forearms (Fig. 8-21).

When lifeguard B is ready, he should give the instruction to lift the casualty out of the water.

As the casualty is moved onto the pool side, trained person E should take over support of the casualty's head from lifeguard A. Trained person E should position the hands over lifeguard A's hands. Then lifeguard A can remove his hands gently by sliding them out from under the casualty.

In the final stage of the recovery, lifeguard B and trained people C and D can slide their arms and hands out from under the casualty. Trained person D removes his hands first, then C and finally lifeguard B. Once all the supporting hands have been removed, trained person E remains in the supporting position at the casualty's head with firm control (Fig. 8-22).

SAFETY DURING SPINAL RESCUES

As we have discussed in Chapter Five, poor lifting technique can cause injuries to the rescuer as well as the casualty. Lifeguards should be aware of this risk and always lift in such a way as to minimise it. They should also be aware of the provisions of the Manual Handling of Loads legislation and the other legal obligations set out in Chapter One.

At some pools, a high freeboard (the distance between water level and the pool side) may make it very difficult to lift a casualty horizontally without a spine board. This problem should be addressed by the pool operator and be covered by the pool's EAP. Even with the casualty on a spine board, high freeboard is still a problem and may call for additional team support. For instance, it is recommended that two people should be on the pool side to accept the spine board, one either side of the board at the shoulder position.

TEST YOURSELF

1. What are the possible results of a spinal injury?

2. Name four classes of paralysis.

3. Why is teamwork so important in spinal injury management?

4. What is a vertebra?

5. What links the individual vertebrae?

6. Where is the coccyx?

7. What part of the spine is referred to as cervical?

8. Describe the relationship of nerves to the spinal cord.

9. Name the two types of nerve.

10. What are the symptoms of a spinal injury?

11. What is a flexion injury of the spine?

12. What is the first priority in dealing with a suspected spinal injury?

13. How would you apply the vice grip?

14. What is a spine board used for?

15. What is the minimum recommended number of team members required to use a spine board?

GLOSSARY

ABC Airway, Breathing, Circulation

Adam's apple A colloquial term for the cartilage which protects the larynx (voice box)

Airway The passage through which air enters and leaves the lungs

Artery A vessel (tube) which takes blood away from the heart

Asphyxia Insufficient oxygen reaching the blood

Asystole Complete inactivity of the heart

Ataxia Irregularity of movement due to defective muscular control

Athetoid Type of cerebral palsy where there is frequent involuntary and jerking body movement

Body core Central parts of the body away from the surface, including the major organs such as the heart, lungs and liver

Brachial Referring to the upper arm

Buoyancy jacket Jacket with minimum buoyancy of 6kgs used for inland and supervised aquatic activities

Bystander A person present at an emergency situation who may be able to provide assistance when requested to do so

Capillary A small, thin-walled blood vessel

Carbon dioxide A gas, found in very small amounts in the atmosphere but in higher concentration in the air expired by breathing

Cardiac Referring to the heart

Cardiac arrest The condition where the heart is no longer pumping blood around the body

Cardiopulmonary resuscitation (CPR) Combined rescue breathing and chest compression

Carotid artery The main artery running up the side of the neck, hence carotid pulse

Casualty A person in difficulty at an emergency situation who needs assistance

Cervical Referring to the neck

Chest compression Rhythmical manual pressure on the chest

Choking Partial or complete blockage of the upper airway by a particle of food or other foreign body

Coma Deep, unrousable unconsciousness

Contact rescues Methods of recovering a casualty from the water in situations where rescue aids are unavailable or unsuitable for use

Core temperature The temperature of the body core, normally 37°C in healthy adults

Coronary thrombosis Blockage of an artery on the surface of the heart by a blood clot, which results in damage to the heart muscle (heart attack)

CPR CardioPulmonary Resuscitation

Defibrillator A device for delivering an electric shock to a casualty to correct ventricular fibrillation

Diabetes A disease in which the body is unable to handle sugar and other carbohydrates correctly

Diaphragm A dome-shaped muscle which separates the chest from the abdomen

Drowning Death caused by asphyxia due to immersion in water

Drowning, dry Drowning in which no water reaches the lungs

Drowning, near Survival of a casualty after immersion in water

Drowning, secondary Fluid in the lungs due to irritation by inhaled water

EAP Emergency Action Plan

ECG Electrocardiogram

Electrocardiogram A recording, usually on a paper strip, of the electrical activity of the heart

Epilepsy A condition in which abnormal electrical discharges in the brain cause seizures

Expiration Breathing out

Expired air ventilation Sometimes abbreviated to EAV, this is another term for rescue breathing.

Fibrillation See ventricular fibrillation

First aid The initial or emergency help given to a casualty before qualified medical assistance is available

Flume A long water slide

Focal point Fixed point on the pool side to which casualties should be brought

Fracture A break in a bone

Heart attack Coronary thrombosis

Heart failure Failure of the heart to maintain an adequate circulation of blood

HSE Heath & Safety Executive

Hyperventilation Deliberate or involuntary series of deep breaths in rapid succession which decrease the level of carbon dioxide causing dizziness or unconsciousness

Hypothermia Reduction in the body's inner core temperature to 35°C or below.

Inhalation The process of inhaling

Inhale To breathe in

Jaw lift Method of obtaining an airway without extending neck

Land based rescue Method of recovering a casualty without the rescuer entering the water

Laryngectomy Surgical removal of the larynx (voice box)

Larynx That portion of the airway in the upper neck which contains the vocal cords, also called the voice box.

Life support Resuscitation of an unconscious, non-breathing casualty

Lifeguard Qualified professional or volunteer employed to supervise and provide safety cover in swimming pools or open water locations

Lifesaver A person who is prepared to assist anyone in difficulty or has ensured the safety and survival of a casualty

Manikin Realistic resuscitation training model

Non-contact rescue Method of recovering a casualty using a rescue aid without making direct physical contact

NOP Normal Operating Procedure

Oesophagus A muscular tube which acts as a food passage through the chest from the mouth to the stomach, commonly called the gullet.

Oxygen A gas, essential for life, which makes up about 21 per cent of the atmosphere

Plasma The fluid part of blood

Pneumonia Inflammation of the lung, usually caused by an infection

Post Traumatic Stress Disorder Physical and emotional disorder caused by excessive amounts of stress

Pulse Impulse felt in an artery with each beat of the heart

Recovery position The position in which an unconscious casualty is placed to allow observation of breathing and prevent obstruction of the airway

Rescue breathing Blowing air into a casualty's mouth or nose to provide oxygen when breathing has stopped (often called expired air ventilation or 'the kiss of life')

Rescue Method of recovering a casualty in difficulty

Respiration Breathing

Resuscitation The act of attempting to revive a nearly dead or apparently dead casualty

RoSPA Royal Society for the Prevention of Accidents

Shock Failure of the circulation which results in an inadequate supply of blood to vital organs

Skeleton The framework of bones which supports the body and protects the internal organs

Spasm Sudden involuntary muscular contraction

Spinal cord The column of nerve tissue extending from the base of the brain down through the spine

Sternum The flat bone, forming the front of the chest, to which most of the ribs are attached, also called the breastbone.

Stroke Damage to the brain due to an interruption of part of its blood supply

Suffocation Obstruction of the airway, preventing an adequate amount of air reaching the lungs

Supine Lying face upwards

Support tow Method of towing where lifeguard supports casualty under the armpit keeping the casualty's head clear of the water

Thorax The chest cage

Trachea The semi-rigid tube, felt in the front of the neck, that takes air from the larynx into the chest

Tracheotomy A hold made in the trachea (windpipe) to allow breathing when there is obstruction of the upper airway

Vein A vessel (tube) which takes blood back to the heart

Ventricular fibrillation Irregular, ineffective twitching of the ventricles of the heart which produces no circulation of blood

Vertebra The individual bones of which the spine is made up

In-water rescue Method of recovering a casualty where it is necessary for the rescuer to enter the water or launch a craft on the water

FOR YOUR NOTES

FOR YOUR NOTES

The Royal Life Saving Society UK is Britain's leading water safety and drowning prevention organisation. Despite the enormous increase in water based leisure activity, the number of drownings in Britain has steadily declined since our foundation in 1891. However, several hundred people still drown each year. We believe even one drowning is one too many, so the fight to save lives must go on.

Ensuring the safety of swimming pool users is a vital part of our mission and we are the premier provider of training for pool lifeguards. Our National Pool Lifeguard Qualification programme is widely recognised as the professional benchmark for the sport and leisure industry. We train up to 20,000 swimming pool lifeguards each year and, together with the Surf Life Saving Association of Great Britain, we also train beach lifeguards.

Promoting life support skills in the community is another important aspect of our work. One in three Britons will suffer a heart attack at some time in their life. Our programmes aim to teach resuscitation techniques to those who need them most. We train up to 250,000 members of the public annually and produce a range of training publications.

RLSS UK is a self-financing registered charity. Our work depends upon the dedication of our supporters, members, volunteers and the generosity of benefactors and corporate donors and sponsors.

YOU can help us to save lives. Please use the tear-off form opposite to become a supporter of RLSS UK. Alternatively, write to us for details of full individual membership.

Simply fill in this form

**I WISH TO BECOME A SUPPORTER OF RLSS UK
(Annual Fee £6.00)**

Title   Mr / Ms / Miss / Mrs / Dr   (Delete as appropriate)

Forename(s) _____

Surname _____

Postal Address _____

_____

Post Code _____

AN EASY WAY TO PAY

PLEASE TICK AS APPROPRIATE

I enclose ☐ cheque ☐ postal order   (Payable to RLSS UK)

Please debit my account

I wish to pay by   ☐ Access   ☐ Mastercard
                     ☐ Visa   ☐ Switch

Card No ☐☐☐☐☐☐☐☐☐☐☐☐☐☐☐☐

Issue No ☐☐☐☐   Expiry Date ☐☐☐☐

Cardholder's Signature _____

**Please send completed form in an envelope addressed to:
RLSS UK, FREEPOST, P.O.Box 3, Studley, Warwickshire B80 7BR
(No stamp required if posted in UK or Northern Ireland)**

Thank You For Your Support

Simply fill in this form

**I WISH TO BECOME A SUPPORTER OF RLSS UK
(Annual Fee £6.00)**

Title   Mr / Ms / Miss / Mrs / Dr   (Delete as appropriate)

Forename(s) _____

Surname _____

Postal Address _____

_____

Post Code _____

AN EASY WAY TO PAY

PLEASE TICK AS APPROPRIATE

I enclose ☐ cheque ☐ postal order   (Payable to RLSS UK)

Please debit my account

I wish to pay by   ☐ Access   ☐ Mastercard
                     ☐ Visa   ☐ Switch

Card No ☐☐☐☐☐☐☐☐☐☐☐☐☐☐☐☐

Issue No ☐☐☐☐   Expiry Date ☐☐☐☐

Cardholder's Signature _____

**Please send completed form in an envelope addressed to:
RLSS UK, FREEPOST, P.O.Box 3, Studley, Warwickshire B80 7BR
(No stamp required if posted in UK or Northern Ireland)**

Thank You For Your Support

- Each year, RLSS UK members volunteer up to 1,000,000 hours of service to the community.

- Each year, RLSS UK brings the skills that save lives to 250,000 members of the public.

- Each year hundreds of lives are saved.

- Each year, RLSS UK trains 20,000 swimming pool lifeguards. Our National Pool Lifeguard Training Programme has over 2,000 Pool Lifeguard Trainer Assessors, 200 National Trainer Assessors and 28 Area Co-ordinators.

- RLSS UK needs YOUR support to continue this vital work and sustain our various training programmes. . .

we can't save lives without YOUR support

This is your invitation to
BECOME AN RLSS-UK SUPPORTER

See over for details

© RLSS UK Registered Charity No. 1046060

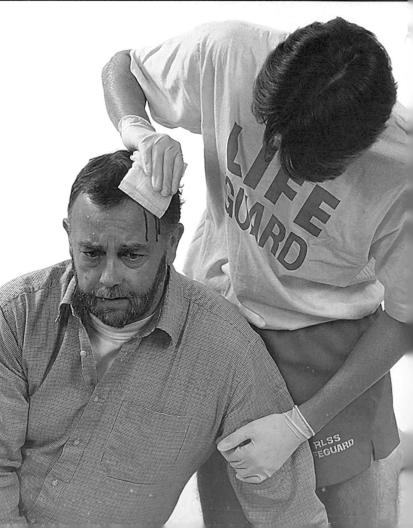